HEADS

A Day in the Life

HEADS

A Day in the Life

GERRY ANDERSON ❧

Gill & Macmillan

Gill & Macmillan Ltd
Hume Avenue, Park West, Dublin 12
with associated companies throughout the world
www.gillmacmillan.ie

© Gerry Anderson 2008
978 07171 4445 7

Typography design by Make Communication
Print origination by Carole Lynch
Printed and bound in Great Britain by MPG Books Ltd,
Bodmin, Cornwall

This book is typeset in Linotype Minion and
Neue Helvetica.

The paper used in this book comes from the wood pulp
of managed forests. For every tree felled, at least one
tree is planted, thereby renewing natural resources.

A CIP catalogue record for this book is available
from the British Library.

5 4 3 2 1

'Commercialism—the ability to do well what ought not to be done at all.'

GORE VIDAL

W hen she turned to face us I could see she was almost pretty. Maybe a tad on the freckled side for me but nevertheless not the usual boot-faced, dropped-arsed dragon we habitually encountered during our regular forays into the lightly manned pharmaceutical emporia found in the semi-deserted small towns and villages that God had sprinkled across this ancient land of saints and scholars.

That same bounteous Saviour had blessed this girl with a healthy, ruddy complexion, a small pip of a button nose, kindly but wary eyes and a dense thatch of fiery red hair corralled and piled steeply on top of her skull to form what I believe is known internationally as a 'beehive'.

She had been busily popping small white pills into some manner of porcelain vial when I bundled a reluctant Eddie into the shop, triggering the door-top bell, which pinged piercingly.

Eddie didn't care too much for this kind of work but accepted his fate stoically, realising that his presence was essential as bait. Shortish and cuddly, he projected an aura of vulnerability that urged civilians to trust and, indeed, warm to him immediately. Unavoidably, he was necessary for tasks such as these. Sometimes things went wrong, but not often.

And even if they did, what the fuck? It wasn't a crime, was it?

The colleen absent-mindedly raised a delicate hand to indicate that she would be free from her immediate task and with us shortly. I steered Eddie towards the counter and shuffled off towards a corner display unit where I fumbled with a bottle of Lucozade whilst casing the joint.

She appeared to be alone. Perfect.

Eventually dispensing with the dispensing of her pills, she turned to face Eddie and placed the palms of her hands on the glass counter top, leaning on it heavily.

I could see that she had copped immediately that Eddie wasn't a local. My guess was that not many of the rampant young bucks in this village habitually wore ankle length fur-trimmed figure-hugging over-coats over a tie-dyed vest, tucked into sky-blue loon pants embroidered with a random selection of large and small red stars, and a pair of crocodile-skin cowboy boots finished off with silver toe-tips. Throw in a wild tangle of unruly blonde curls, a tiny gold ring dangling from one pierced earlobe and you've more or less got the picture. In other words, a handsome swine if ever there was one.

Nevertheless, the girl behind the counter seemed blithely un-impressed.

Not for long, I thought.

Eddie turned on the Smile as I arrived by his side. The boy was a natural. He gave it to her full beam: lazy eyes slightly hooded, perfect glowing white teeth, a casual toss of the mane. It was the smile of an eight-year-old child: open, innocent, warm, trusting, unwittingly sexual, rehearsed to perfection and artificial to the core. Women were powerless in its path. This is why he was delivering the spiel and not me. I had the wrong kind of teeth for this kind of close-range work. I was proud of the lad.

She lowered her eyes coyly.

'Lovely evening,' purred Eddie.

'Isn't it just, so?' she replied, fumbling in the pocket of her white shop-coat for what turned out to be a crumpled white linen handkerchief. She dabbed her nose delicately but kept the hanky clutched in her hand. Good sign.

'May I help you at all?' Her voice had adopted a higher pitch.

She was on the hook.

'You may, indeed,' breathed Eddie, looking deeply and meaningfully into her eyes. 'May I have a small packet of Elastoplast and a jumbo box of Kleenex tissues, please.'

He smiled again. A few more teeth on display this time. Good boy.

Her face flushed as she shyly glanced away, fiddling nervously with a brown paper bag that rested on the counter.

'And a bottle of Lucozade,' added Eddie, moving his face a little closer to hers, leaning forward and resting his elbows on the glass.

'No need. I have the latter to hand as we speak,' piped I, approaching the counter in a business-like manner, brandishing a cellophane-clad bottle containing far too much of the vile liquid.

'There you go!' laughed Eddie. 'We're hardly any bother at all, are we?'

'Not a bit,' she giggled, and skipped off happily to assemble the other items he had requested.

Her return was my cue to cough loudly and sniff heavily, to give the impression that a seemingly awkward amount of putative sputum was lodged uncomfortably at the back of my throat. I gagged theatrically and clutched my nose.

Go now, Eddie.

He was on the slow side today. I had to nudge him with the toe of my boot.

'J-J-Jaysus!' he finally exclaimed. 'You really should get something for that trouble of yours while we're here.'

The girl seemed alarmed and looked at me for the first time. 'Sounds nasty. What's wrong with you?'

'Ah… sinuses blocked,' I gasped. 'Strikes every once in a while…' (splutter). 'Poxy pollen gives me gyp…' (sniff). Don't suppose you'd have anything that would relieve a man's discomfort, sinus-wise?'

She moved swiftly to her right, opened a glass cabinet, brought out a small box and placed it on the counter.

'Try one of these Vicks nasal inhalers. It'll give you some relief. Clear out the pipes.'

'Wish I could, luv,' sez I. 'Can't use those Vicks jobs. Allergic to them.'

Gurgling, gasping theatrically for air, I nudged Eddie again with the strategic foot.

'W-w-what about the ones you got up North,' said Eddie. 'They worked, didn't they?'

I bent over almost double and clutched Eddie's shoulder for support, 'Can't get those down here, boy,' I gasped. 'Wish I'd stocked up last time we were up in the Quare Place.'

'Nasal inhalers?' enquired the girl, seemingly alarmed.

'Yes,' spluttered I.

'What class of an inhaler was it?'

'Oh, different type altogether. German, I think they were…' (honk). 'Arcane ingredients. Worked a treat…' (snarf). 'Say what you like about them, the Krauts know their onions.'

'What were they called?' she asked. 'We might have them. You never know.'

A helpful girl.

I was snuffling well. Snuffling for Ireland. Time to recover now. My work was almost done here.

I straightened myself up and wearily dragged a tissue across my brow. 'Don't remember the name of them. Only used them the once. Do you remember what they were called, Eddie? Benylin? Benelum? Something like that? Started with a "B"?'

'Yeah,' said Eddie. 'There was a 'z' in it too. Benzedin? Benzedum?'

The girl's face suddenly lit up. 'Benzedrex, was it?'

Bingo.

'The very boys!' I crowed. 'How did you know?

Her hands were fluttering. Excited now. 'Just remembered seeing a box of them. The owner of the shop keeps them in the back room. He said they don't sell well. People don't like the smell of them.'

A fatal flaw in a nasal inhaler, I reflected.

Those people didn't know what they were missing.

She disappeared behind a beaded curtain.

Eddie waited until sure she was out of earshot and flashed me a mixed look of pain and unease. 'Go easy on her,' he hissed. 'She's a nice girl. She'll be sacked when her boss finds out.'

'She won't be sacked,' I snarled. 'And even if she is. What the fuck?'

Back she bounded, happily toting a largish box.

'Here we are, lads!' she trilled. 'There's more of them in here than I thought. You may as well have a couple while you're at it. Stock up? Wasn't that what you said?'

'Are they expensive?' I enquired. 'Probably much more expensive down here than they are in the North.'

'Not a bit,' she laughed gaily. 'Only eighteen pence each. Cheap at the price.'

'I'll take them all,' I said, crisply, naturally, without hesitation.

Go for broke, I say.

Eddie gnawed his lip and shot a nervous look at the girl. She seemed a little taken aback, but not as much as she should've been. God bless her innocent, untutored heart.

A small uncertain laugh. 'But there must be nearly two hundred of them in the box. Think you'll need that many?'

Best to be brusque. 'Can't take that chance again,' I said. 'Look what happened last time. Better looking at them than looking for them, wha'?'

Time to adopt a swift business-like approach before she put two and two together.

I swiftly fished a battered wallet from my pocket and peeled some notes from a slender stash.

'Forty quid should cover it, eh? Just throw everything in a couple of those big paper bags.'

She hesitated slightly. 'But, wha…?'

'Don't forget the Lucozade and the other stuff. It's time we were gone. Aren't those the lads beeping the horn up the street, Eddie?'

He cocked a pantomime ear. 'I do believe it is.'

She hesitated momentarily before handing over the bags. There was a short awkward silence. Eddie leaned over and kissed her cheek whilst I slapped the four tenners onto the counter and snatched the bags from her grasp. 'Tidy pharmacy you have here. It's a credit to your community.'

We edged towards the door. 'Thank you. Must fly. Throw the residual change into the poor box. Every little helps. There are people tramping the roads who can't afford to buy pharmaceutical goods. What this country needs is an all-embracing national health service. God bless you and all belonging to you.'

She opened her mouth to speak but it was too late. We were gone. The reverse ping of the doorbell announced our departure and we were on the street.

2

It was difficult to find useful drugs in early-seventies' rural Ireland. Let me qualify this by declaring that we didn't operate at the hard end. We were barely more than dabblers. Softish drugs merely provided a bit of variety to a daily regimen that traditionally relied heavily on alcohol. I was never much of a drinker though and consequently marginally keener than the other guys in the band on finding an alternative. To them, the quest for mild drugs was little more then a diversion, a faintly interesting way of passing the time. The cooperative young lady's rural dispensing pharmacy was the fourth we'd tried that afternoon. We'd been readily rumbled and speedily dispatched from the other premises by worldly bespectacled gentlemen wearing white coats who, quite understandably, didn't like the look of us.

As drugs went, Benzedrex inhalers were crude and non-life-threatening when taken in moderation. But, I suppose, like everything else in this world, they could kill you if you tried hard enough, but then again, as cannot be denied, so could holy water, air, jelly babies or ice cream. All one requires is the will to go further and to push the envelope.

The inhalers suited us fine; a cheap and ready source of pure Benzedrine, the substance with which the firm cotton wad nestling within the plastic casing of the artefact was heavily impregnated. When four or five of those babies were immersed in a receptacle containing a minimum of two fingers of household Coca-Cola, then firmly squeezed and left to settle for a few minutes, the resultant evil-tasting cocktail would stimulate the nervous system to a point where a man's heart would pound like an alligator's, his energy know no earthly bounds and he would babble nonsense for at least twenty-four hours, neither desiring nor requiring sleep for at least twice that time-span.

In short, the stuff kept us awake longer than was good for us. Advanced users usually chewed the cotton wads straight from the plastic case, like Mayans gnawing on the coca leaf. A strong stomach is required for this approach. Furthermore, as proof that God enjoys a laugh every now and again, the average rampant male with an enthusiastic benzedrine habit soon learns that familiarity with the chemical tends to instil in the user an intense desire to pursue women even though fully aware that an erection will not be forthcoming.

This is an unfortunate by-product of the drug, known to sufferers as the Benzedrine Drawback. Drinkers will recognise this as a variant of Brewer's Droop or the more ancient 'Porter Hinge'.

Temporary impotence was not a subject widely discussed within the confines of the showband world. Some things were best kept to oneself. But life was complicated by this unfortunate side effect. It had seemed hitherto unthinkable to indulge in any recreational activity that ruled out the possibility of casual sex. After all, everything we did, even our individual decisions to become musicians in the first place had, in most instances, been informed by the theory that we would become more popular with women.

Nevertheless, the immediate buzz of the drug was almost worth it.

We usually compensated by talking too much to each other about fuck all.

For my part, Benzedrine made me more outgoing and sociable. I once introduced myself individually to each member of the queue waiting to see the *Dirty Dozen* outside the Savoy Cinema in Cork City. All fifty of them.

As far as I recall, my reason for doing this was to jabber at them about having seen the film myself in Dublin a week previously. I felt the need to inform them that Lee Marvin was a cunt and told them how the film ended.

It seemed important that they know.

———

It was 1972 and I was playing bass guitar with a showband of sorts, trading under the rather pedestrian name of 'Brown and O'Brien', a moniker that recalled a solicitor's firm in Sligo rather than a functioning musical outfit. At this point in my life I was ensconced in a bed-sitting room situated just off the South Circular Road, in Dublin, in the vicinity of Leonard's Corner, where a man could procure a plate of sausages and mashed potatoes, with gravy optional, at two o'clock in the morning. I was also surrounded by many similar apartments providing shelter for a fine selection of female nursing students and girls who were too wild for the small villages and hamlets from which they'd fled.

The Manhattan Café was important in the general scheme of things, especially for someone like me who did not cook, would not allow food of any kind to cross the threshold, and never felt hungry until after midnight. The Manhattan Café was built with me in mind.

Discreet and filthy on the outside—a maggoty exterior, windows bisected by peeling wooden slats – the interior décor was not designed to encourage people to linger: randomly scattered, grimy, Formica-topped tables, rusty tubular chairs and a big, high, wooden, wood-wormed panelled counter behind which lurked the shrill harridans who grudgingly ministered to the needs of small-hours' show-band heads and assorted drunks stricken by the False Hunger.

When I first came to Dublin fresh from the bosom of my family home in Derry it didn't occur to me that I should eat at all, preferring, as I did, to drink vodka and smoke untipped cigarettes. Barely more than a teenager, I regarded food as something that was given to one by one's mother, something to be dispatched speedily before lurching off to do other things. Nutrition was not a word that figured in my vocabulary. Food was so plentiful in our house that I never knew what it was like to experience even the slightest pang of hunger. I never felt like eating any-thing, having always just eaten something moments before. I ate because I felt I was expected to do so. Alcohol and tobacco were different.

Things came to a head one Friday night when I collapsed onstage at the Top Hat Ballroom in Lisburn in front of a shoeless Sandie Shaw. I was revived by brandy and recovered sufficiently to finish the gig, only to collapse once more the following night immediately after com-pleting a spot on the *Late, Late Show*. I remember little about the incident other than that, behind the scenes, Gay Byrne didn't seem at all the friendly, loveable little man whom the nation knew and loved. At rehearsals that afternoon, I sensed in him a quiet anger worthy of the disappointed Christian Brother that he so reminded me of. He pursed his lips in distaste at the sight of us cluttering up the studio and demanded that we be removed from the premises whilst he rehearsed another item.

However, I did learn from this in years to come when I, too, sadly, became a television chat show 'host'. Just as a country is judged by the way it treats its older citizens, so is a talk show host judged by the way he treats the band, especially when one of its members is on the point of collapse.

Before Gaybo had gushed an oily goodbye to his misguided adoring studio audience, I was already horizontal and semi-conscious. I was rushed to the Mater Hospital where a young physician of a dusky hue announced that I was suffering from a mild dose of malnutrition, the first he'd seen outside the Dark Continent.

He told me that it was important I have access to food. I thought sausages, mash and gravy would do just fine. I moved habitat to be close to this dish and my health gradually improved. I also ate the occasional apple or portion of citrus fruit to avoid the onset of scurvy.

I did not cook in the flat because my television set sat on the gas cooker's four rings. If placed anywhere else I couldn't see the screen properly when in bed.

I would not allow food to enter the room, (a) because it left a lingering odour and (b) because my fridge contained dirty socks and a top hat. Tip: when one's socks remain on one's feet for more than two weeks and consequently become a little whiffy, it is not necessary to wash them and create the unsightly spectacle of wet socks hanging forlornly on a wire or line. Just pop them in the fridge for a day or two, after which time they may be worn without nasal odour-detection for another week. Repeat the procedure, *ad infinitum*, until one's socks disintegrate completely. Then buy a new pair.

I owned no furniture and made do with what I found when I moved in. My worldly possessions consisted of one acoustic guitar, a three-bar electric fire (bought under duress during a particularly virulent cold snap), a number of old band suits and two newish ones (bought cut-price from a Jewish show-band tailor in a Pearse-Street basement who thought I was the right shape to wear his clothes. He lovingly fashioned the only four-piece tweed suit in Dublin that I was aware of at the time: trousers, jacket, waistcoat and three-quarter length overcoat), sundry shirts, one pair of shoes and a number of seldom-troubled books. In later years I donated the four-piece suit to my Uncle Manny in Donegal. The last time I saw this tweed creation was him wearing three-quarters of it whilst ushering his cows back from the local meadow which they daily frequented.

Otherwise, I travelled light.

I had a top hat which also lived in the fridge. The lower temperature kept it cool and crisp. I wore it when playing my guitar and when entertaining visitors, whom I preferred one at a time.

I learnt about the ritual importance of headwear from a friend of mine who scraped a meagre living writing musical arrangements for showbands. He wore an Arranging Hat whilst at work, a small, trim trilby. Without it on his head, he could not adequately function. This seemed to me a good idea, I'm not sure why.

I owned no car, had no surplus cash or savings of any kind, owned no property and made no provision for the future.

I was twenty-two years old, feckless, fond of music, women, an occasional drink and whatever else happened to rear its head.

I was a full-time musician in a business where people lose their jobs overnight. I lived as if tomorrow would never come.

I was told that some day it would all end. I took no heed.

I couldn't have been happier.

But the showband boom was tailing off, bad news for people who cared, but of little consequence to Brown and O'Brien. We weren't much of a showband anyway. Our hearts were never in it. Showbands have to care to be successful. The punters can smell apathy.

I was inordinately fond of this Dublin though not best pleased that the 'Troubles' in my native North were reeling out of control. Dubliners were just beginning to develop a healthy dislike for people from Up There. It was not always thus. When I first came to live in Dublin in 1966, we Northerners were regarded as almost, well, exotic. Seems strange now but Dubliners once perceived us as better-educated, healthier, significantly more advanced culturally and therefore, I suppose, almost cool. Being categorised as nominally British, I suppose we were regarded as a shade sainted, having access to goods and services not yet readily available to those beyond the Queen's bailiwick. What Dubliners didn't realise was that many of us were Down Here because we had been treated like shite all our lives Up There. However, on the plus side, we had marginally better teeth and could drown in a sea of condoms if the notion took us.

I had noticed with some satisfaction that Dubliners habitually referred to inhabitants of other parts of the Republic of Ireland as 'culchies' but as yet had no generic term for Northern Irelanders. We were not the 'Nordies' that we are now. They had no idea how odd we were.

——

I and my fellow members of Brown and O'Brien were gathering in Dublin prior to making our way to a gig somewhere in Donegal. The exact location was unimportant to us, as we had long since ceased to care where we went. Except to collectively hope that the gig was not an integral part of a carnival. If, to our chagrin, this proved to be the case, we would perform in what is known as a marquee.

Basically a large tent, this sprawling, hazardous, temporary structure would be erected by the local parish council during the summer months for the purpose of holding hopefully profitable dances for the benefit of parishioners. Amongst those expected to attend were the timid, the cocky, the forgotten, the spurned, the superannuated, the mentally handicapped, the crippled, the lame or the merely halt. These dances were usually part of some broader village or town festival. There are generally two types of marquee tents—two-polers and three-polers—although every once in a while it is possible to encounter the rapidly disappearing four-poler—the Tyrannosaurus Rex of this esoteric canvas world.

Two-polers are relatively bijou but marginally more dangerous, the broad expanse of the canvas routinely trapping rainwater in the centre and at each end of the sagging, swaying roof—rainwater generated by the summer monsoons. As bands like ours were usually called upon to perform on a makeshift stage situated at one or other end of the tent, gazing down upon a temporary, sawdust-covered slatted wooden floor, nervous musicians habitually spent long anxious hours standing directly underneath untold gallons of suspended water whilst surrounded by, and often wired directly to, functioning electrical equipment. The prospect of instant death was never far away.

At least with the electric chair, a person gets to sit down.

These marquee dances were generally well supported. On a busy night, the interior of a typical tent was a nightmare of crushed bodies, cheap perfume, crippling body odour, the primeval reek of long-worn underpants mingling with the familiar stench of recently consumed alcohol and freshly minted puke.

On one side of the tent gathered frightened, beehive-headed women who appeared to be wearing somebody else's clothes, on the other, a heaving mass of damp, sullen, inebriated, randy men wearing dark suits.

Facilities were not ideal. Men, like livestock, pissed and shat outside in the field. None of us was quite sure what the women did—there was a small, isolated tent well away from the Big Top that no-one talked about.

We usually changed into our shiny suits in a crudely fenced-off designated area, a quagmire situated just behind the stage, unaccountably muddier than anywhere else.

We didn't look forward to marquee dances, always regarding time spent under these canvas awnings as a gentle reminder that we were living and working in the wrong country.

The last tent we'd visited was situated just outside a small village called Kilnaleck, in Co. Cavan. It was a Sunday as I recall and, passing through the hamlet, we blearily discerned, through the steamed-up windows of our horseless carriage, a certain degree of uncharacteristic hustle and bustle generated by what turned out to be the annual festival's fancy dress parade. Later that night the chore of doling out prizes to winning contestants was entrusted to the band. I, being the Talking Head, was allotted the task. In time-honoured reverse order, third prize was announced first. This coveted prize, of a small box of Black Magic chocolates, went to a peculiar looking man who lurked at the rear of the tent. He was short in stature, owning a very large head blighted by bulbous growths on both fiseóg and skull.

He was also, alas, the custodian of an unfortunate hunched back, and displayed a marked tendency to growl at anyone who looked at or approached him.

His prize-winning fancy dress costume consisted solely of a roughly torn-off square of cardboard upon which was scrawled the legend, 'Paddy's Got A Tiger In His Tank'. This alluded to a popular advertising slogan of the day, a slogan lost in the mists of time, something to do with petrol, as you may or may not recall.

Otherwise, he was conventionally dressed in a soiled light blue suit, two sizes too small, probably purchased by a relative or friend who had bought it during a mad moment in Manchester or Birmingham. This ensemble had probably been proudly worn by a number of people, each for a decade or so before it had somehow filtered down to him, the last stop on its long journey to the finality of the rag store.

I bawled into the microphone and summoned him to the stage. He responded immediately and tottered forward to embark upon what turned out to be a long and painful trip to the front of the stage. He was forced to face the gauntlet of hundreds of high-spirited men and youths, all of whom seemed intent on landing a heavy blow on his person. Most of them succeeded admirably. Those who didn't strike him with their fists felt the need to kick him, usually in the vicinity of the bollocks, or, as I once saw reported in a local newspaper, the 'forkal region'. *Craic*, I believe it is known as in the Old Tongue.

Anyway, by the time he reached us, within range of my giving hand, he was pretty well fucked, actually bleeding here and there and on the verge of losing whatever degree of consciousness he had enjoyed at the beginning of the evening. He crawled towards me on all fours, like a mud-skipper experimenting with dry land, whimpering softly. I offered him the small box of Black Magic chocolates and watched them tumble gently from his feeble grasp. Rustic guffaws emanated from the rough-neck bastards who surrounded us, still sporadically lashing out at his crumpled person.

Fearing him badly injured, I managed to attract the attention of a disinterested bouncer who, under protest, carried him into the mud-flats that passed for our dressing-room. He reluctantly promised that Paddy would receive some rudimentary medical aid.

Ten minutes later, I left the stage and peered behind to ascertain that the patient was still alive. I was informed that he had recovered and left. He was last seen making his way down the road on his bicycle—whistling, apparently.

A hardy breed indeed.

Famine genes, I'll bet.

This was life in the wild. Dances in tents were a law unto themselves. We saw the inside of so many that I often felt like a Bedouin tribesman.

Sometimes local beauty queens were paraded in the tent to be judged Carnival Queen, a dubious honour at the best of times, judging by the menace generated by the pissed, salivating, panting youths who, knuckles brushing the ground, rushed the stage at the merest hint of the swirl of a skirt.

These beauty queens were usually sponsored by local hostelries and, consequently, proudly bore the title of the establishment represented. A young lady, for example, could find herself known as e.g. MISS TRAVELLER'S REST for a calendar year.

But there were worse fates in store for young girls hungry for a title. I have always found the young ladies of Donegal particularly unfortunate when it came to representing their local watering holes. We can well imagine severely restrained or, at best, muted celebrations on the part of a young girl's parents upon receiving the news that their daughter would be known for the next twelve months as MISS SQUEALIN' PIG.

Likewise, MISS AGONY PIPE.

And pity the young lady who triumphed at a particular motel in Letterkenny. What wouldn't most young red-blooded men give for a night with MISS THREE WAYS?

And then there is the Queen of them all. A beauty queen named after the Donegal village in which she lives. May there be a MISS MUFF forever.

No wonder we craved a little stimulant now and then.

———

My average day didn't usually start until lunchtime and today was no different. I was due to link up with the band at the usual 'call' rendezvous outside our manager's office on Harcourt Street. Donegal bound, we planned to hit the road at about 2.30. There was a time when this meant that I didn't need to get out of bed until two o'clock.

These days, I gave myself a leisurely two hours' preparation time. This granted me an ample hour or so to force down (still no trace of an appetite) a life-preserving lunch and also accidentally to bump into the stunning medical student who lived in the flat two doors down from my airless hovel. She hailed from the Indian sub-continent. The greyness of Dublin only succeeded in rendering her more beautiful than she would have been if she'd stayed at home. Golden-skinned, red-lipped, almond-eyed, sari-clad and wary of strangers, I found her highly desirable. I had been stalking her for weeks. There were cultural differences to overcome.

She was friendly, outgoing and totally impervious to my increasingly desperate pleas for a date. I comforted myself by assuming that her inevitable refusal was the consequence of some externally imposed colonial barrier that prevented her from associating with the white man, and would not bring myself to consider the unacceptable alternative, i.e. the strong possibility that she didn't like me.

Her non-responsiveness worried me somewhat, considering that I was having a similar lack of success with the airline hostess who lived in the flat next to mine. Judging by this plane-jockey's more or less regular stream of gentleman callers and the sound of the unrestrained creaking of bedsprings and coital grunts penetrating the thin walls, she seemed significantly less chaste than my trusty Indian companion.

I encountered her often in the hall, a tall, thin but sensual wisp of a girl with a sly eye and a cruel, attractive smile. I fancied her greatly in the most visceral of ways and often invited her into my lair for a nightcap and a peek at my top hat. She invariably laughed and refrained.

Her lack of interest disturbed me, especially as half the men in Dublin seemed to have formed the habit of regularly fucking her. And I observed some of these men who came to call, even opened the front door for some of them occasionally. They seemed no great shakes to me.

I was experiencing a crisis of confidence that I hoped would soon pass.

Given the benefit of hindsight, it's alarming to think that nearly everything I did then was determined by the habits and location of various women in whom I was carnally interested.

I habitually lunched in a spartan Rathmines café situated just below the Stella Cinema. I did not, of course, wish to eat lunch. As far as my lack of appetite went, tea and a sliver of toast would suffice. However, to my great credit, I do believe I learned my lesson after my fainting fit. Considering my medical history of susceptibility to wasting diseases, a goodly intake of stodge was advisable before heading off into the heartland where, even if we arrived with time to spare, slim hopes of a meal on arrival at the gig were often cruelly dashed. I needed to keep my strength up. After all, I had already battled malnutrition and did not wish to extend my experience of Japanese prisoner-of-war maladies in these northern latitudes. Let beri-beri and dengue fever remain in the swamps and rain forests where they belong. After all, it's what De Valera would have wanted.

There was another reason why I liked to lunch in Rathmines. In another world, my father was once based at Portobello Barracks just down the street. He had run away from home in 1924 to join De Valera's boys, anxious to do his bit to help restore order where chaos had previously reigned. He was seventeen years old. He didn't stick it for long and, when reality kicked in, he returned home healthily disillusioned, aware early that none of those who commanded him gave a toss about the Free State or about whether he lived or died.

Years later, in the fifties, when I was but a nipper, my father took me to see a visiting, elderly President De Valera stumble blindly through the gorse on his way to pay homage to the old Gaelic fortress of Grianan of Aileach in Donegal, followed by thousands of the slavering faithful.

The decrepit Dev's grasp of the white man's magic was still firm. Still blinded by the almost-blind man, how my father's eyes shone with remembered pride. I was held up to see the Old Artificer.

My father had patrolled these streets when he was much the same age as I am now. I like to think that maybe he, too, sought the company of Indian medical students and nymphomaniacal flight attendants.

But the Moving Finger writes and, having writ, moves on to a place that serves lunch.

There were two further reasons for my choosing this Rathmines eatery, (a) a house speciality of pork chop, peas, mash and gravy and (b) a dry-cleaning emporium on the other side of the street in which laboured a very healthy girl called Gillian who regularly came to frolic with me when her long-term boyfriend travelled across or down the country to practise his trade as a peripatetic plasterer, something he did on a commendably regular basis. Hence lunch provided a frisson of risk. I always half expected to spot the plastering cuckold striding manfully across the street baying for my blood.

Just a fleeting of glimpse of Gillian was enough to activate the loins and set me up for the day. She was twenty-two years old, brunette and voluptuous. She was also wonderfully immoral and enthusiastically promiscuous. She dry-cleaned my shirts and gave me a considerable discount.

We were, of course, never seen out together. When her boyfriend was away she stole her way to my 'studio' under cover of darkness. That was the way I liked it. No boring chitchat in the pub surrounded by arseholed rugger buggers. She complained that her boyfriend wasn't keen on any form of oral sex. As a warm-blooded mammal, I was encouraged by this.

Rathmines was more like a village then. People knew each other and each other's business. The two spherical ladies who waitress in the café whispered about me and knew what was going on.

Although mildly disapproving, they were never less than courteous and generally kept to themselves as I silently munched lunch and trained a gimlet eye on the dry cleaners.

They sometimes asked quietly if I wanted more chips.

I frequently said no.

It strikes me that if it wasn't for music and women, I'd never have got out of bed at all.

3

The hour of two o'clock found me within the shabby but relaxing confines of the Abbotsford Hotel in Harcourt Street, an accommodating bolthole of choice for musicians and actors, resting or active.

I was sitting in the company of one of our band's two eponymous lead singers, Billy Brown, sadly now no longer on this earth, but in July 1972 a magnificent specimen of raddled masculinity and ruined talent. He was carelessly but impressively turned out in ersatz country-squire garb: herring-bone jacket, cavalry twill trousers, and clasping his calves were the kind of dull, long, brown soft leather riding boots that didn't look like much but couldn't be purchased for less then a month's wages. He was wearing an open-necked checked shirt with a tucked-in relative of a cravat which was, in truth, more of a gypsy neck scarf, or bandanna, as those of us weaned on cowboy movies would describe it. He had a handsome oval face, aquiline nose, troubled eyes and a fine thatch of long straight light-brown/blond hair, parted centre skull that swung freely down and brushed his shoulders.

Although a tall, lean and charismatic fucker, Billy was a casualty of this business, chiefly because he possessed remarkable musical talent. From the mid-sixties onwards he had achieved great success with a band called the Freshmen, an outfit from the North that specialised in reproducing Beach Boys' hits on stage better than the Beach Boys could. He had, however, a nasty streak of creativity that circled him like a buzzard. The earning of large amounts of money had, as my mother used to say, got the better of him, dragging the man down to a determinedly dissolute life dominated by swift cars and fast women.

My ambition was to be dragged down there too, but money was tight at my end.

Billy found it difficult to break out when natural law decreed he should. A move to England a few years before might have gained him a wider audience and the recognition he deserved but it was too late now. Ireland was not yet a place from which one could launch an assault upon the lucrative English pop charts (the Irish charts were for the most part rigged and regarded as a joke by all except the paying punters, which is indeed a cruel life lesson in itself), unless you happened to be the poxy Dubliners. That's the way it was then. Ireland had long lost any sense of itself except for the usual small band of writers and poets drinking themselves to death in selected pubs that were not yet crawling with American tourists in search of the ex-hang-outs of gifted grumps like Patrick Kavanagh. The Roaring Tiger lay way in the future, Billy was condemned to listlessly fade away, eking out the still-plentiful shillings that remained to be gleaned from the musty ballrooms of this backward land.

He was also that most rare of human beings, a man with a stammer who loved to talk—a man with much to say who found it almost impossible to speak. His stammer was a mystery to me in that it had no definite pattern. No specific vowel or consonant was guaranteed to grind his verbal flow to a halt—all were equally treacherous. He would often glide effortlessly over words that commenced with obviously deeply difficult letters like 'S', 'R' or 'W', only to be felled by a word beginning with the innocent 'E' or equally benevolent 'I'.

Billy would then shut down completely whilst he went through the prolonged agony of retrieving the rogue word from wherever it had inexplicably gone. This involved spirited twistings of the neck, the audible grinding of molars and silent clenching of fists. These tortuous silences often endured for up to a minute, by which time the initial point of the cruelly interrupted sentence had generally evaded the listener.

Crucially, despite the handicap of what used to be known as a stutter or 'stoppage', he was a sophisticate, fond of art and opera. Patience was normally advised when Billy endeavoured to communicate, and restraint normally exercised when one felt the urge to help him complete his sentences. He didn't like people putting words into his mouth. I don't suppose you would either.

He had made the mistake of leaving the 'Freshmen' and forming his own band, ostensibly and naively for the purpose of pursuing more money and artistic freedom, the jagged, ill-matched rocks upon which many of his ilk had foundered.

This misguided foolishness resulted in the 'Billy Brown Superband', a bunch of malcontented but generally accomplished musicians and singers carefully selected from the usual flotsam and jetsam tradition-ally found in Dublin. This outfit embarked upon a circuit of the country's ballrooms playing a mixture of finely crafted jazz-based power pop that was musically head and shoulders above what any native outfit had previously aspired to. The venture was, of course, doomed from the outset.

One lap of the dance-hall circuit was more than enough.

Dancers countrywide slithered to a halt and gazed up at the band with the bovine stare that seasoned show-band musicians know so well. The punters had become aware of the absence of the show-band chop, a peculiar pulsing but clipped off-beat, known to the aficionado as the 'Galway Wallop', also familiar to the more astute as the Heartbeat of Ireland. And there does indeed exist such a primeval regular thud, a particular tempo to which rural dancers (and many city folk too) seem genetically programmed to respond. This deep irresistible urge is something older than ancient, its preternatural origins buried in the mists of a lost Celtic past via the moan of Moorish quarter-tones and the squeal of the Scottish bagpipes.

But enough of that ethno-musicological bollocks.

Suffice to say that certain things will remain as they always have been, until they become unfashionable. These ancient ways will then seem to disappear, only to lie dormant until the time comes for them to resurface with renewed vigour.

Even today, in New Fussy Ireland, in smoke-free pubs from which all character and curiosity has been otherwise sucked, but wherein survive the tired remnants of country bands, the alert observer may still divine small, square, squat, masculine women of a certain age sporting Nazi-helmet hairstyles, instinctively leap into automatic jiving mode when the Galway Wallop thunders forth, like the hallowed bellow of some great lost ballroom hunting horn. But the tempo must be exactly right to activate the voodoo. The slightest nano-second too slow or fast and these women will fail to respond. Something preternatural within them will reject the signals. Nor will they even hear the music. We're talking here about the beat that activates the natural jiver. It's primeval and sacrosanct. As old as the legend of Cúchulainn.

In layman's terms, it's a case of count the bastard in, no fancy stuff, give 'er the holly and the divil take the hindmost.

Billy's band was a musically sophisticated outfit. They were dead in the water.

He should've known better.

His new and desperate management then cajoled him into re-creating something that sounded and looked something akin to the ultra-successful Freshmen in a bid to keep the financial ship afloat. Gathering together a bunch of itinerant jobbing pop musicians, of which I was one, under the moniker Brown and O'Brien, we played the ballroom circuit with little or no enthusiasm. We were neither liked nor disliked.

It was worse than that.

We were ignored.

———

The two of us brooded silently now in the Abbotsford Hotel nursing the dregs of a couple of large brandies. We were staring dully at an elderly drunk actor wearing a pork-pie hat. I recognised him as a man who played a major part in an RTÉ television soap called *The Riordans*.

He had a round, pockmarked face that was discoloured and flushed to within a hair of a heart attack. A network of thin dark veins were visible on his flabby jowls where they bunched and snaked down his neck until they disappeared beneath the grubby collar of a once-white shirt which was partially and mercifully concealed by a horsey-man's red waistcoat streaked with cigarette ash. He looked like a man suffering from fatally high blood pressure who'd be lucky to be alive this time tomorrow. For reasons that I failed to fathom, he was railing about the dangers and pitfalls of keeping ostriches.

He waved a lit Senior Service cigarette in a dangerous arc. 'Never make the mistake of standing in front of them bastards,' he advised the barman, a defeated, slight man who coughed heavily and often.

'You think you're safe when you're face-to-face with the fuckers but you're not. You're safer round the back staring at their holes... where you think you wouldn't be safe at all! They're not like fuckin' horses or fuckin' donkeys, you know. They won't ever kick you if you stand behind them. It's the way their legs are conflig... conflug... configgerated or whatever the fuck you call it. Never stand in front of the cunts.

It's more natural for them to kick you in the bollocks when you're facing them. They flick their big horny feet forward, you know? They like to look you in the eye when they lash out. It suits the angle of their legs, the big, ah, drumsticks, you know?'

'You catch it in the privates if you stand in front of them, then?' muttered the bored barman, peering at the ceiling through the glass he was polishing.

'Fuckin' right! They kinda flick at you with their big fucking toes. Big nails on them too. But you're safe enough if you're behind them.'

He then inexplicably burst into song. It was, of course, 'The Auld Triangle.'

The act of singing caused him to wobble. The ageing thespian struggled to maintain the perpendicular.

Billy shifted uncomfortably in his chair. 'Everybody in this town's Brendan f-f-f-fuckin' Behan,' he grunted, impatiently swirling half a finger of brandy round the bottom of his glass.

Billy seemed a mite edgy for the time of day. This hotel tended to bring out the worst in him. The old place had seen better days which, of course, was the source of much of its charm. It was, in short, a kip. But a kip with character.

Dense carpet, peeling wallpaper, abused furniture and an aura of smoky decay rendered it just fine by me. I shuddered to think what the bedrooms might be like, especially when acquainted with the knowledge that they could be rented by the hour.

The establishment was loose and louche.

It suited us well.

The last time I'd been on these premises with Billy, it was at the rear end of a bender of a couple of days' duration. Having arrived at that dangerous point where the drink was no longer enough to keep him awake, he had refuelled with a variety of uppers, always a dangerous path for a tired man carrying emotional baggage. His domestic affairs in the North were somewhat in disarray. He had, of course, fallen for a younger woman and abandoned the older model and young family just as he was becoming accustomed to the flush of money and a relatively prolonged period of popularity. This type of behaviour is not unusual in show business. In some quarters it is regarded as mandatory.

He seemed, however, inordinately attached to a baby grand piano housed in his erstwhile family home up in the Quare Place. Mumbling incoherently about driving up North to retrieve the treasured instrument, it was some time before I could convince him that there may well be practical difficulties involved in forcing a baby grand piano into the back seat of a Lotus Elan.

Billy also had a problem when it came to paying maintenance to his first spouse. When we played gigs in the North it was not unusual to discern the discreet, dark presence of a representative of the discredited yet, nevertheless, still-in-charge Royal Ulster Constabulary anxious to have a word with the lank-haired singer.

Thus did Northern gigs emit a whiff of danger and suspense.

The singing actor from *The Riordans* suddenly listed to starboard but miraculously swung back upright by means of that wonderful accomplishment of evolution, the inbuilt gyroscope that prevents drunks from falling over as often as they rightly should. But, sure, don't we all have our crosses to bear? A couple of large brandies in the early afternoon in the company of singing drunken actors obsessing about ostriches can set a man's mind to thinking.

I found myself wondering how the fuck I'd ended up humouring distressed singers who wished to fit baby grand pianos into the back seats of small, powerful, expensive cars.

4

I suppose it was all my brother Johnny's fault. For reasons that mystified the rest of my family, he bought himself a trombone. He was twenty-one years old at the time—a late starter. I was a mere fourteen, a normal contented child with a healthy lack of ambition and no sign of a developing work ethic.

Johnny referred to his trombone as the 'horn'. Soon, a number of musicians who regularly played in Derry's Embassy Ballroom (a plastic-and-glass monstrosity situated just around the corner) became frequent visitors to our home. They would roost in our claustrophobic communal kitchen drinking numberless cups of tea, smoking heavily and laughing heartily at things I only half understood, speaking reverentially of mysterious, and often regal, icons such as Cannonball, Monk, the Duke, the Count, Dizzy, Miles and Bird. They wore thin white socks with black patent leather shoes, mohair suits, dazzlingly white shirts, string ties and camel-hair overcoats. They didn't seem to trade under conventional names and referred to each other as 'head', as in, 'Nice horn, head.' 'Toss me a fag, head.' 'Catch ya later, head…'

I was mightily impressed but unsure why.

I discovered later that the origin of the term 'head' might conceivably lurk in the old-time musical practice of using what were known as 'head arrangements'. This was the practice of putting together hasty, on-the-spot arrangements of tunes, i.e. by listening to the records and figuring out the parts by ear, rather than labouring over prohibitively expensive pre-prepared written musical scores or, more commonly, 'orchestrations' or 'orchs'. But who knew?

Initially, the sobriquet 'head' was applied to a musician who was particularly adept or talented. The expression 'he's a head' meant that the person referred to was special. And old-timers in the music business still used the word reservedly. In short, the term had to be earned. Of course, when things changed and the young pop whippersnappers got in on the act, the word 'head' somehow morphed to refer in a general manner to anyone who was a member of a showband, period.

These young 'uns appreciated fuck-all.

The heads who came to my house spoke in what was almost an American accent, not a tongue normally associated with those born in the Bogside. No fool I, I attributed this to the existence of the permanent American naval base in the Waterside area of Derry. As far as the heads were concerned, the American base was Paradise itself, a microcosm of the fable that was America, where wonders such as pizza, Budweiser beer, real hamburgers and Lucky Strike cigarettes could be procured with unaccustomed ease, especially if one was a member of a band that had managed to get a gig in the Enlisted Men's Club or, even, better in the Officer's Club, where, incidentally, the range and identity of the visiting local female talent on display was as surprising as it was pulchritudinous. 'Nice' girls weren't invited onto the base. The Yanks were no fools. Members of the band made mental notes.

Once a musician became a familiar face on the base, he could wheedle access to the PX, a kind of home-from-home store where naval personnel could purchase most goods that were available in New York or Los Angeles. To the heads, that meant the latest jazz records from the States, priceless gems treated with the utmost reverence and ferried about tenderly from home to home like Padre Pio's mitt…

Clothes too. Black leather jackets with red stripes down the arms, purple shirts, white shoes, blue slacks, yellow socks—the pick of Stateside vulgar beauty.

The heads were American all right, in everything but nationality.

Musically, they flew by the seats of their immaculately pressed American pants.

These men reeked dangerously of aftershave lotion and Brylcreem.

After much practice in the attic, Johnny soon became a card-carrying head himself. Our house was permanently imbued with the slightly sickly odour of Old Spice and the rafters rang with firm demands for a clean white shirt every night.

More heads appeared during the day, vanishing at dusk.

Johnny seemed to enjoy his new role as a *bona fide* head.

This status was confirmed at eight a.m. one Monday morning as my father and I silently enjoyed our traditional glum breakfast of tepid porridge, tea, and heavily buttered toast.

I heard the thud of a slammed front door, succeeded by a muffled oath. The kitchen door flew open. A trombone case clattered to the floor and shot smoothly across the worn yet highly polished linoleum. I beheld Johnny standing in the doorway, staring at his brother (me) and his father with strange glazed eyes. At the third attempt, Johnny succeeded in removing his camel-hair coat and made an ill-judged lunge at the over-subscribed coat-hook that was nailed to the back of our kitchen door. The coat connected with the hook but unfortunately Johnny neglected to loosen his grip on the garment. He slithered slowly to the floor. At a crucial point the coat-hook disengaged itself from its moorings, causing many other coats to cascade and pile upon the by-now-horizontal trombonist.

My father seemed to notice none of this, casually pouring himself another cup of tea from the big, brown pot.

I remained resolutely silent. I knew I was witnessing something unique.

From the corner of one eye, I saw Johnny's arms flail the air blindly from beneath the mound of clothing. Eventually disentangling himself from the twisted garments, he crawled slowly on all fours towards the kitchen table and somehow hauled himself upright onto a chair, neck muscles straining valiantly due to the great effort involved. Settled vaguely upright now, his head lolled from side to side, glasses comically askew at the wrong end of his nose, his bow-tie out of kilter and the collar of his white shirt daubed with what I realised later could only be lipstick.

To my bulging, though not entirely innocent, eyes, he looked like a person who had recently had a very good time indeed.

He also looked ill. Greenish.

'Cup of tea, son?' my father softly enquired.

'Yesh, plis,' muttered Johnny, now sitting unnaturally upright on his chair, white-knuckled hands gripping the side of the kitchen table.

'Help yourself,' my father said breezily. And a little mischievously, I thought.

Johnny blanched. He was now less green.

Brow determinedly furrowed, the visage a grim mask of determination, he reached for the teapot. Curling his nicotine-stained fingers carefully around the warm handle, he somehow managed to steer the business end towards the cup and fill it almost to the brim. He had done extremely well. Maybe he could go all the way.

Now he stared dully at the three-quarters-full milk bottle standing tall in the centre of the table. I feared that this might well be a bridge too far.

One eye closed to facilitate accuracy (he still did this, even though he had lost one eye in a childhood accident. Habit I suppose. He always closed the sightless eye, I need hardly mention), he managed to grip the bottle with the spindly fingers of a gently trembling hand.

At this point, crucially, all motor skills seemed to desert him. The bottle slipped from his grasp. I held my breath. The vessel bounced once and zigzagged crazily across the table spewing out milk in a treacherous creamy torrent. Most of the liquid landed on my lap, the rest splashed onto the kitchen floor, much to the delight of our cat, Pssst (it didn't have a name. Only a sound).

My father sighed loudly, rose slowly and walked wearily to the kitchen sink where he washed his hands with a degree of deliberation. Pontius Pilate, I thought.

My school trousers were sodden. They would be rank soon.

Unfazed by this breach of etiquette and wanton spillage, Johnny stretched his arms lazily and yawned in an exaggerated comic-book kind of way.

'Lookit time tis,' he almost managed to say. 'Time t-t-t-turn in.'

He hauled himself to his feet and immediately listed to port, treading heavily on the cat's tail.

The resultant feline shriek prompted him to hurriedly place an index finger on his lips, the way drunks do in the movies.

'Shhssh, Pssst.'

He reeled towards the door and was gone.

I heard him fall heavily on the stairs, the tumble punctuated by a foul oath.

My father dried his hands on a well-used towel.

He leaned in my direction. I could smell the shaving cream.

'Let that be a lesson to you, boy,' he whispered.

But it was too late. My mind was already made up, my destiny clear. I had decided to become a head.

5

By the time we heard the come-hither toot of the coach parked on the other side of the street, the crumbling actor from *The Riordans* had marginally recovered and was midway through a spirited though deeply flawed rendition of 'The Black Velvet Band'.

Billy was a little glassy-eyed by now and had grown quiet.

These were pressing times for a sensitive soul. He had recently begun to dabble in water-colour landscapes, often a worrying sign of withdrawal from the world.

Times were not good. The country was changing and the showband business was in freefall.

Prior to the late fifties, the flowering youth of Ireland had remained resolutely subservient until awakened and kick-started by the evil that was rock 'n' roll, causing alarm amongst upright citizens and incensing the ruling clergy who were distracted momentarily from buggering the children of their parishioners. City elders were outraged by the sight of young people, fired up by cannibal music from a film called *Blackboard Jungle*, jiving spontaneously in streets that had been paved for decent people. In the fullness of time, hips were self-consciously swivelled in draughty bedrooms and hair sinfully tampered with, Brylcreemed and pompadoured. In rural areas the music was corrupting the young by means of faint foreign radio but still not yet heard in parish halls where the restless had little choice but to listen to rusting sit-down bands and witness the stiff perambulations of mature slow-waltzers and fox-trotting older bogtrotters.

De Valera's Ireland was still alive, healthy and fast asleep.

The dominant colour was grey. If an acne-scarred youth wanted to buy himself a red shirt like the one worn by Elvis, he'd have to fly to Naples.

Something had to give. There was a gap in the market due to the dearth of rock 'n' roll music on Irish radio (there was no RTÉ... yet). Frankie Byrne and Larry Gogan were waiting politely in the wings.

Furthermore, due to the fact that charting British and American groups were not in the business of touring this green and pleasant land, some manner of substitute was required.

The showband was born.

A showband is basically a 'cover band' that reproduces pop music for a live audience. This was no new phenomenon. Cover bands existed (and still do) all over the world forming a minor but necessary part of any country's musical culture. Cover bands are normally nurseries where musicians cut their teeth musically and learn how to comport themselves on stage. Only in Ireland did they become ends in themselves, and only in Ireland did the cover bands became more popular than the chart-bothering artists whose music they copied. And, uniquely, influenced by the instrumentation of the earlier sit-down bands, showbands evolved to adopt, as standard, the classic Dixieland jazz-band line-up i.e. keyboards/guitar, bass guitar, drums, trumpet, saxophone, trombone and expendable 'lead' singer.

Showbands became phenomenally popular. In their mid-sixties' heyday they were the focus of the transforming social life of the nation. What was then known as the 'dancing public' (many of whom had rarely travelled more than twenty miles from their homes) would forsake what remained of the crossroads action and travel long distances to see men from other parishes grin and jump, encased in cheap shiny suits.

It may not have been what De Valera had in mind.

Breezeblock behemoths of ballrooms were hastily constructed throughout the land to accommodate the restless young and not-so-young, all of whom hungered for this new live second-hand music. These great mausoleums, usually erected in the middle of nowhere, were primitive, draughty, cold and alcohol-free, much like the country in which the punters lived, except for the last bit.

Thousands followed Dickie Rock and the Miami for a glimpse of Dickie's curled lip. Countless hordes travelled great distances to see Brendan Bowyer sweat and aimlessly swing his seldom-blown prop trombone.

How they hooted at Joe McCarthy idiotically fucking about on drums with the Dixielanders.

But, by the late sixties and early seventies, the novelty had begun to pall and, as the public began to demand more from a night's entertainment than a bottle of freezing lemonade gulped down in a wind-blown corner of some custom-built dungeon of a grimy dance hall, the showband business began to slowly expire.

Those determined to persevere endeavoured to delay the inevitable by introducing bizarre novelty as a means of hanging on to the rapidly disappearing punters.

A band called The Indians (miraculously, they still survive) appeared on stage dressed as Apaches, complete with war paint and decorative feathers, no doubt plucked from the vulnerable arses of fleeing barnyard poultry. Tomahawks were employed in tandem with other random, gerry-built ethnic paraphernalia designed to stimulate the jaded clientele.

The singer, 'Big Chief', could be regularly observed warbling Neil Diamond's 'Sweet Caroline' wearing ceremonial headdress and unaccountably waving what appeared to be a conventional household hatchet.

An outfit trading under the name of Wee Mick and the Hootenannies employed a singing dwarf as front-man. The kernel of their act involved poking merciless fun at the cheerful homunculus (who busied himself jauntily walking a wooden plank that jutted precariously from the stage, whilst simultaneously employing a small, potent water pistol to squirt an unidentified liquid at the ogling punters). The band's manager kept himself busy by using a long stick periodically to prod the shortened singer. And, oh yes, it was reported that Wee Mick sometimes wore a small motley with tinkling bells attached to the hem of his costume.

The Zulus extracted a living by appearing blacked-up from head to toe, resplendent in grass skirts that doubtless housed the occasional shamrock. They were also in the habit of brandishing home-crafted assegai spears at the confused dancers. I once had an interesting, though necessarily strained, conversation with an African medical student who found himself witnessing their act.

He didn't have much to say about the entertainment provided.

Tarzan and the Monkeys mined the same freakish seam. Legend had it that Tarzan once managed seriously to damage his body by launching himself from the balcony on a rope suspended from the ceiling. He reputedly earned himself a spirited round of applause and considerable kudos by managing to crash into a set of ancient iron radiators as he flew towards the stage. There was hushed talk of severely damaged ribs and permanent injury.

The Monkeys wore ape suits and lumbered exaggeratedly about the stage, knuckles trailing the floor. They grunted at the punters. Bananas were de rigueur. The Hollywood Stars dressed as movie icons and historical figures. The unconvincing 'Marilyn Monroe' had mottled legs, and hair that had seen bottled hydrogen peroxide once too often. A coonskin-hatted Davy Crockett tootled the trumpet and a curiously out-of-place Robin Hood manned the drums. Julius Caesar played the saxophone and at least had the good grace to appear embarrassed when the girls standing in front of the stage jostled for a shuftie up his toga. The Godfather sulked behind his trombone refusing all offers.

The Phantoms wore Spiderman-like clinging bodysuits and masks. The leader of the band once told me that the masks were a boon for two reasons (1) he could fire people at will and replace them without the punters noticing the personnel change and (2) the musicians were free to sign full-time on the dole without running the ever-present risk of being spotted on stage by over-zealous government officials.

This was the milieu in which we operated during those summer months of 1972.

6

In spite of the depths to which showband heads were sometimes obliged to sink in order to keep themselves in drink or to ensure that their children were fed on a daily basis, and whether or not they were driven to take the stage wearing a grass skirt whilst unenthusiastically wielding spear, tomahawk or dwarf-bothering stick, and no matter what catalogue of humiliations they were destined to endure, I always imagined that these adverse circumstances would never really succeed in extinguishing what initially drew them to the music itself. But maybe I'm a dreamer. I always imagined that, no matter how cynical a man becomes (and I'm taking a risk by including session musicians here) the initial spark or trigger that makes a man yearn to become a musician in the first place will seldom expire completely. The memory of it may dim and lie dormant for years, but it will always lurk deep in the subconscious, capable of surfacing when least expected.

There are, of course, many exceptions to this rule. For the insecure, becoming a musician is fulfilment of a need to be noticed; for the randy, a way to meet women; and for the optimistically rapacious, a means of making lots of money. The last tend not to linger long in the front line and usually slink like skunks into management, a role in which, as they'd hoped, they become fat, false, ruthless and unpleasant to know.

As for the rest, and I'm referring here to the innocent and the blessed, their fate is often sealed in one seminal moment when, at an impressionably early age, a piece of music they hear on radio, television, the concert stage, bandstand, music hall, opera house or street corner will sear their souls, changing them forever. It may not necessarily be one of the greatest pieces of music in the world, indeed it may just be a snatch of something mundane that grips the imagination—but to the listener it's a moment of magic. A certain accumulation and fusion of these moments is usually what plants in a person's mind the desire to become a musician.

As a child I experienced extraordinary musical moments, seated as I habitually was on the round wooden box-like structure, crudely fashioned from an old tea-chest that acted as a cover for my mother's sewing machine. Perched thus (I still have that sewing machine and the cover, which bears the dent made by my embryo arse) I reached the elevation necessary to cock an ear close to the old-fashioned radio set positioned halfway up the kitchen wall on a shelf supported by sturdy brackets.

My father insisted that this radio be situated high up and out of reach to prevent children like me interfering with the knob that changed the station, a knob that was semi-permanently and worryingly tuned to either Radio Eireann or Athlone—opinion differed in our household as to what the station was actually called. Not that it mattered.

When I did manage to wrest the knob to the vicinity of the interesting though often pompous BBC, I found myself seriously smitten by the theme music from a radio series called *Journey Into Space*, which featured an actor called David Kossoff (father of Paul Kossoff who, coincidentally, later became lead guitarist with a band called Free and played one of the best guitar solos of all time on an early-seventies' hit called 'All Right Now.' He eventually, and fittingly, killed himself with drugs) playing the part of an astronaut called 'Lemmy' in an episode called 'The Red Planet', during the course of which the planet Mars was tentatively explored and discovered to be less barren than was previously supposed. Lemmy was, and remains, the only aurally identifiably Jewish astronaut I have encountered thus far. His distinctive speech patterns were so imprinted on my consciousness that, later in life, whenever I talked to Soho or Hollywood music fixers of a Jewish persuasion, their vocal inflections ensured that the canals of Mars were never far from my mind.

But I digress.

An updated random selection of magical moments include the glorious cymbal crash on 'So What' by Miles Davis, a seemingly endless silken *swooooosh* that kicks off the improvisational end of things; the stuttering majestic drum break on Stevie Wonder's 'Superstition'; the elementary guitar riff on Johnny Kydd's 'Shakin' All Over'; the introductory organ on Bob Dylan's 'Like a Rolling Stone'; the late entrance of the bass guitar on Ike and Tina Turner's 'Nutbush City Limits'; the piccolo trumpet on the Beatles' 'Penny Lane'; the jangle of Paul Brady's guitar on 'Arthur McBride' (Bob Dylan eventually recorded 'Arthur

McBride.' Made a bollocks of it, of course, as I knew he would. But the fact remains that he liked the song enough to sing it, and that was enough for me); the sliding double bass on 'Walk on the Wild Side', the lyricism of Van Morrison's 'Madam George', the force and genius of Charlie Parker and the rock 'n' roll attack of a fiddle in Donegal played by the right man in form and in his prime.

Moments like these, and no two men's moments are the same, bend a person's mind and entrance him or, indeed, her into contemplating life as a musician. Later considerations such as world travel, drink, money and sex with minors make themselves known along the way, and are not initially relevant. The urge to play is the driver.

Corruption and disillusionment take root later.

My true introduction to this wider world occurred in the early sixties when a local Derry showband, of which I was barely a member, decided to undertake a six-week tour of England from which it was destined not to return.

As I had recently been fired from a job on Derry's docks which involved early mornings and strained relations with stevedores, I regarded this Lenten tour of Irish clubs in England as a welcome diversion.

I was barely a member of the band because I wasn't initially an asset to them. Joining as a guitar player (my brother Johnny had put in a word for me) they soon discovered that I was incapable of solo work. I was basically a chord man. As they say, rhythm was my business (I'll explain later). In other words, I was an oddball.

They should've sacked me immediately but they didn't. They kept me because of Johnny. In a bid to render me useful, they offered me the bass player's gig. This change of tack required but a slight adjustment, the four strings of the bass guitar (as every schoolboy knows) sharing the same tuning as the bottom four of a conventional six-string guitar—no heavy lifting required. Their long-term but now ex-bassist was an elderly, exhausted man who pretended to play stand-up double bass fiddle (the first and last bass fiddle I ever encountered in a showband. It is possible to pass oneself off as a double bass player if one cannot actually play the instrument at all. It requires a strong hand, brass neck and a confident expression. As long as one produces a steady dull thud all will be well). He'd decided he'd had enough, tiring of young whippersnappers entering the business. I consequently got my hands on a cheap bass guitar and muddled through as best I could. The end result wasn't earth-shattering but my enthusiastic efforts seemed to justify my existence. Nor was I much of a strain on the band's finances. My needs were few. The important thing was that for the first time, I felt part of a band, a head. As time progressed, I eventually developed a certain fondness for the bass guitar, a fondness that developed into an interest bordering on an obsession.

I'd never been to England before. A showband 'tour' of England is the same as a 'tour' of America or Canada; a series of scattered gigs in undesirable locations usually sustained by a homesick Irish population, some of whom tended to feel less isolated if they paid money to gawk at and jive to the music of men who owned faces fresh from the Old Country. There is no difference between an Irish club in New York and one in London: same furniture, same pictures on the wall, same punters, and the same air of bleakness and general despair.

Showband 'tours' of England were usually undertaken during Lent, the dogma of the Catholic Church being so all-pervasive in the early sixties that opening a dance hall during this period of sustained abstinence was tantamount to trampling the Eucharist underfoot. People cared about being branded an atheist or blasphemer then. I knew grown men who actually worried about the possibility of being excommunicated from the mother ship. They generally misunderstood me when I informed them that I ran no risk of such punishment as I had already excommunicated myself on a voluntary basis.

I would often urge them to do likewise.

Such talk was, of course, blasphemous and warranted a prolonged sprinkle of Holy Water. I know that now…

Because showband heads had, courtesy of a regional God, no means of making a living for six weeks during that Holy Season of Lent, they were driven perforce to England or further afield where, apparently, the locals didn't hold with the Holy Season of Lent. What a geographically specific and precise Saviour had we. There were other places similarly blasé about Lent. Horrible Scotland was toured when all failed. Wales was never even considered. We Irish have never taken to the Principality of Wales. Too much like home.

The dancing punters in Erin were innocently unaware of the economic pressures that forced Irish showbands to tour England, so pains were taken to reassure them that their favourite bands toured outside the country purely because there was international demand for their services. To this end, much false publicity was generated to demonstrate that our popularity was global. It wouldn't do to give the impression that the celebrated stars of the contemporary Irish music scene were traversing the length and breadth of Britain with the sole aim of earning a mere workman's wage. It was important to look and act as if we were beyond that stage.

When I was a member of The Chessmen circa 1969/70 (we were reported to have had numerous hits on the Continent of Africa (in Voortrekker territory only), and were allegedly selling records in Sweden.

Whilst a member of a quite different band, I and the other minstrels were once summoned to Dublin Airport on a sunny August afternoon where a photographer issued each of us with small but empty overnight bags. He then instructed us to line up in formation beside a large functioning aeroplane bearing the logo of a major international carrier. We were photographed waving goodbye prior, I assume, to boarding, en route to some exotic destination which we were destined never to reach.

When the shoot was over we were advised to catch a bus back home before dark.

English 'tours' usually involved bivouacking in London, where Irish clubs had long blossomed in Kilburn, Cricklewood, Harlesden and the like. There were, of course, furtive trips to Manchester, Liverpool, Birmingham and worse.

The clubs were owned usually by gruff men who had prospered in the construction business, men who knew much about the human condition and the value of a shilling. These blighted venues were a refuge for the lonely, the disaffected, the alienated and the badly dressed. I felt sorry for the emigrant male of the species. As a body of men, they seemed doomed, with or without the benefit of alcohol. It was the Diaspora at play. Men culturally marooned.

The women seemed better equipped to cope with life in England. This may have been partially down to the fact that English men were carnally interested in Irish women, whereas English girls generally had little time for Irish men, especially those just off the boat. The odds were stacked against these hapless males, especially those from rural areas in Southern Ireland (the Northern and Dublin Lads did better. Because they had been through more hoops at home, the shock of the new seemed less traumatic). An upbringing in bucolic Ireland had rendered the country boys stout of limb, healthy of body, ruddy of mien but woefully unprepared for city life in England.

We were offered a residency in a club in Manchester called 'Shorrocks', now mercifully pulled down and forgotten by all but me.

Run by two flint-hard brothers who majored in the demolition business, it was a venue that took no prisoners. Ramshackle, squat, desolate, and situated in a less-than-desirable area just off Oxford Road, the club had a door policy that operated under vaguely Darwinian principles of natural selection. Only those deemed fit to survive could hope to gain admission. The Neanderthal bouncers on the door operated a policy that I have difficulty describing even now. These sentinels were the type of Irishmen whom I thought had disappeared into the mythology of 1930s' New York movies, fiery violent men whom one could imagine mashing a grapefruit into a woman's face before drilling a slug into the side of her head. Top of the world, Ma!

The best I can do is to suggest that they admitted to the premises only those who most resembled themselves in looks, temperament and the ability to wound. It mattered little if those granted entry were drunk or inclined to violence. They were often both.

If the paying patron punters looked right to the bouncers, that was O.K.

I figured their ideal candidate for admission would be a cross between Christy Ring and Genghis Khan.

No wimp or nerdish figure crossed the threshold.

One can imagine how we in the band felt. However, despite being mostly card-carrying wimps and certainly nerds to a man, we needn't have worried. Treated as special cases, we were regarded by the macho staff as court jesters, organ-grinders' monkeys, not subject to the laws and limitations routinely applied to everybody else.

We were granted permanent fools' pardons.

I also had to deal with something new. For the first in my life I was acutely aware of being regarded as Irish.

I had never before thought of myself as belonging to any particular nationality. In real terms, the concept of nationality meant nothing to me. Because of the peculiarity of the entity that was Northern Ireland, I felt neither Irish nor British. Most people in Derry felt Irish or British. I didn't feel anything. I just existed. Here I am. Look! Over here...

Now I was in a country whose citizens treated me as a full-blown Paddy. I wasn't sure how I felt about that. The Paddies I was being lumped in with were mostly subservient by circumstance and proud by nature. The two didn't mix. I found it difficult to buy into that double-bind and felt equal to anyone.

I resented assumptions that I was thickish and slow. English people whom I met would, when discovering I was Irish, sometimes initially spoke to me as if I were a child. I didn't particularly like being thought of or spoken to in this way. Neither did most other Irish people. But there were those who didn't notice...

I began to understand the way the world worked. It was not unusual to see posters advertising dances in the North of England on which it was specified that Irishmen would not be admitted.

We played four nights a week as resident band, basically playing relief, or support, to visiting showbands. It was an education of sorts in that I realised pretty quickly that these bands weren't up to much and not particularly interesting. I quickly discovered that most showband heads on 'tour' in England, especially those who had wives at home, regarded the trip solely as a wonderful opportunity to fuck everything with a pulse. And there's nothing wrong with that, I suppose. Back in Ireland, they usually had to return home every night, no matter where the gig was. Here they were alley cats and none the worse for it. English tours saved many a marriage. It's healthy to have something to look forward to.

The visiting bands were well supported by the exiles, not because they were particularly talented outfits, but because of the part of Ireland the band happened to be from. The punters just wanted to see fresh-faced men from their own bailiwick. This wasn't about music. It was about identity and belonging. I was learning rapidly.

Thus, because the majority of punters on building sites were predominantly from the West of Ireland, bands such as The Johnny Flynn Showband from Tuam! barely on the show-band radar at home, proved hugely popular in Shorrocks.

Bands from Cork did extremely well too, Dublin bands less so (emigrant Dubliners, like the Nordies, felt more at home in England than the sodbusters) and bands from the North would have been better off staying at home except for the fact that they would've starved there, which is why I suppose we took this morale-sapping resident gig in the first place.

The visits of the more popular bands, or perhaps I should say bands representing the parts of Ireland from which most of the punters originated, occasioned astonishing scenes of drunkenness and record levels of violence. I often cowered in corners aghast at the carnage, brandy and port in hand. I found the ingestion of large brandies and ports the most efficient means of deadening one's senses. This anaesthetic proved expensive before I got to know the barkeeps, after which it became less so, and eventually, to my ultimate cost, entirely free of charge.

When riled, which was too often for my liking, the bouncers would often employ methods of punishment that would have caused even the Gestapo to think twice. I remember one particular act of barbarity involving a harmless drunk doggedly bent on hearing the Dixielanders Showband from Cork. One of the more simian bouncers, for reasons best known to himself, because the punter, to me, looked no different than any other drunken Corkonian, reacted badly to words the inebriate had murmured. Something about the provenance of the bouncer's mother, I believe. The drunk, left-hooked solidly to the chin, sailed down four stone steps and came to rest, unconscious, his head lolling over the lip of the pavement. Not content with having knocked the man out and causing a likely fracture of the skull due to the subsequent tumble, the enraged bouncer tore down the street and scrambled into the driver's seat of his parked car. He gunned the engine, sank the boot and steered straight for the drunk's bobbing head which was, of course, still dangling over the road. The bouncer fully intended to mash the man's cranium under the wheels. An alert passer-by spotted the potential danger and, grasping the drunk's ankles, hauled his inert carcass out of harm's way just as the car's hubcap cannoned across the road due to the impact of one of the vehicle's wheels against the pavement. The hubcap clattered ominously against rusted iron railings.

I made a mental note to consort as little as possible with men such as these.

The only acts who generated broad support that was not specifically geographically based were those who had 'made it' in England. To enter the pop charts in England was the ultimate achievement, especially in Manchester where *Top of the Pops* was filmed in a disused church in Didsbury, not too far from Shorrocks. The Irishman didn't venture there. Too alien. Men who worshipped Dermot O'Brien's sporting reputation and accordion expertise were unlikely to take to a live and mincing Mick Jagger.

Irish nationals who made the charts of this foreign land were rare and sainted, except for Van Morrison and his group, Them, who once appeared in Shorrocks to a mainly hostile reception, having gained a minor toehold in the charts with a song called 'Baby, Please Don't Go.' But this was an exception. I knew in my heart of hearts that Van wasn't Irish club material. We Irish did not yet understand nor realise the significance of modern blues, especially when sung by sullen Ulster Scots from Belfast.

More suitable heroes surfaced. King of the Hill was Val Doonican. Val ticked all boxes. Not only top of the charts in 1964 with a song called 'Walk Tall', but a decent unassuming man from, yes, Waterford. One felt that, had the cards fallen differently, Val would've been on the lump too and likely to part with a bit of his sandwich.

I'm sure there are those who talk still about the night Val Doonican appeared in Shorrocks and not only sang 'Walk Tall', but 'Delaney's Donkey' as well.

It turned out to be a triumph of all that was good and decent. Even I felt a tear come to my increasingly jaundiced eye. His visit was greeted by the kind of wild celebrations one imagines would be accorded a Roman general returning in triumph to the Eternal City after ruthlessly eliminating the threat of Visigoth, Gaul, Thracian, Scythian, Pict or even Brit.

Val was a down-to-earth, likeable man who knew his music. His subsequent enduring popularity came as no surprise. And, surprisingly, I liked him a lot. Here was a better-than-average guitar player who promised to talk to his record manager about our band. He thought we were good. Or maybe he just knew what to say. I was young. I took part in a 2007 BBC 4 television documentary about his career. After it was aired he sent me a nice letter thanking me for my contribution, mannered as it undoubtedly was. I was thrilled to receive it. I'm still a sucker.

The Bachelors appeared too, no less successful in England with enthusiastic ballads such as 'Ramona' and 'Charmaine', but this trio weren't particularly liked by Shorrocks Man. The Bachelors were from Dublin, of course, and looked and acted as if they'd been in England long enough to acquire that patina of show business smoothness that isn't received well in the trenches. They were perceived as being somewhat shifty and shallow, a perception which, after meeting them, seemed accurate enough to me.

The indigenous songbirds came too, the Bridie Gallaghers and Eileen Donagheys, judiciously cracked voices warbling songs of longing, mother and home to a motionless mob that seldom stopped short of shedding a silent tear. Alas, no Ruby Murray. Although from Belfast, she had become too big too soon and had already passed into mythology.

Well into her battle with the bottle by then, her name is mentioned now only in the realm of rhyming slang when men with drink on board decide to order a vindaloo.

But it wasn't all parochial. The occasional international name turned up too. I remember a rather confused Hank Locklin stumbling on to the stage to sing his hit, 'Send Me the Pillow that you Dream On'. He was wearing a gold lamé jacket with an embroidered Irish cottage on the back, complete with lovingly stitched puffs of smoke wafting from the solitary chimney, drifting towards his bull-neck, and the legend CAD MILE FAULTE boldly misspelt just below the collar.

One of the advantages of living in Manchester was the opportunity to see some of the international touring greats, those who would probably never perform in Belfast, or even in Dublin, for that matter, certainly never in Derry, the latter being the extent of my world thus far.

I went to the Free Trade Hall to hear and see Duke Ellington and his orchestra. Not knowing how things worked, I hadn't booked. The majordomo at the door took pity on me and informed me that the only seats available were onstage, behind the band. Nobody who wanted to hear the band properly wanted those seats. I was probably the only member of the audience who preferred to sit behind the band. Elated at the peculiar seating arrangements, I looked forward to feeling what it was like to be close to such a band, I wanted to see how it all worked.

I took up my position and watched the band duly troop onstage. My heart nearly stopped as I recognised, apart from the Duke himself, my namesake trumpeter Cat Anderson and Ray Nance on cornet and violin, saxophonists Johnny Hodges and Paul Gonsalves, drummer Sam Woodyard and all those names that the heads had bandied about in my mother's kitchen at home. All those names of near-mythical status. And here I was practically, no, actually sitting in their midst.

The first thing I noticed as the band settled was a peculiar smell, a smell that seemed to waft upwards to the ceiling. It was my first time to inhale the combined aroma of whiskey and marijuana. I have ever since associated that smell with big-band jazz, and quite rightly so. The scent of the Gods.

I was seated directly behind the trumpet section. The drummer adjusted his kit, the bass player swung his double-bass to the perpendicular, the brass and reeds lifted their instruments to their lips, Sam Woodyard raised a thick drumstick, and waited. An elegantly dressed and wonderfully sophisticated-looking Duke Ellington stared at the band, a little half smile playing about his pencil-thin lounge-lizard moustache. I was expecting him to count in the band in the conventional way or at least indicate that the drummer should do so. He did neither. Cued by just the slightest nod of his noble head, the band miraculously kicked in.

As the music blasted and the players shifted in their chairs, shuffled their music, bitched to each another, farted, sneezed, scratched their balls, played impossibly difficult music, and made faces at Ellington when he wasn't looking, I knew I would treasure this night forever.

Highly memorable too, in a different way, was the visit of the Tamla Motown/Stax Tour to Manchester. There, in the Plaza Ballroom, I stood open-mouthed as Diana Ross and the Supremes, Smokey Robinson and the Miracles, The Temptations, (Little) Stevie Wonder, Martha and the Vandellas and Marvin Gaye took to the stage. The communal backing band was the Tamla Motown house band, the Earl Van Dyke Six. The deep boom of the bass and that peculiar jangling but solid distinctive Motown sound, something that I had previously thought only attainable through recording studio expertise and downright trickery was now, to my astonishment, casually reproduced live on stage.

Token White Man on the tour was Georgie Fame, no slouch himself when it comes to howling a blues or two. I felt sorry for him, having to compete in such celebrated company. I think that he, too, sensed the futility of his task, judging by the hangdog look on his face when he took to the stage.

Poor Georgie was out of his depth, a mere apprentice sitting at the feet of masters.

And so was I.

After both experiences I slunk back to Shorrocks and limbered up for another spirited rendition of the 'Bold O'Donahue.'

I was never going to be in Duke Ellington's band and it was too late now for me to have been born in Detroit.

The cobbler to his last...

7

Of course, I hadn't always been a musician. Back in 1962, I even had a regular job. This was an achievement in itself. I was eighteen years old at the time and playing in a semi-pro band called the Beaumont Seven, a ragtag collection of mostly elderly men who should have known better. A standard job and playing in a band didn't mix.

I would frequently arrive home from a gig at eight or nine o'clock in the morning, often tumbling straight out of the band's creaking van at the entrance to R.A. Burke and Company Limited (Shipbrokers and Forwarding Agents), Londonderry. Just in time to stumble up the dusty wooden stairs to take my place on a high stool at a desk from which flowed all the expertise necessary to ensure the safe passage and welfare of all sea-going vessels that steamed in and out of the port of Derry.

I was customs clerk and dogsbody, often sequestered to do what nobody else cared to. My duties were varied. A person needs to be alert when called upon to hire five taxis for the purpose of ferrying twenty Spanish merchant seamen to the casualty ward of the local hospital, all of whom were smitten by the same venereal disease. From the usual single source.

A man needs a clear head when explaining himself to the duty nurse at reception.

'Hello,' sez I.

'Morning,' sez she.

'Got a few sick men here. Spanish sailors from a ship called the *Richard de Larrinaga*, recently out of Barcelona but now here.'

'And their names?'

'The usual. I've got a list here. Three or four Gonzalez's and a brace of Mendozas. Maybe we could do the paperwork later? There's a time factor involved here. Their ship sails at three o'clock this afternoon. The high tide will not linger. Maybe you could just sort the lads out?'

'How many did you say?'

'Twenty.'

She pursed her lips. 'It'll take some time to examine, diagnose and treat them, I'm afraid.'

'It'll take no time at all to diagnose them,' I replied.

'How's that?'

'Because they've all got the pox.'

'Pardon?'

'Gonorrhoea. It's the big "G" and you will doubtless recommend a swift jab and the devil's little umbrella for the lot of them! If you find a bit more manpower, we could have them processed and out of here in an hour. Remember the old saying, time and tide wait for no inflammation of the genital mucous membrane? Straightforward inside scouring job and an arm full of penicillin. Nothing to it.'

She lifted a pen and stared pointedly down at the notepad on her desk. 'Keep your voice down,' she hissed. 'There are decent people listening.'

And, admittedly, the local outpatients in the waiting room were nervously edging away from the infected, grinning Spanish salts.

I realised then that the job was coarsening me, rendering me blind to the sensibilities of others.

But that didn't mean that I couldn't become the quarry.

One of my other duties involved calculating stevedores' wages. They were a violent bunch, slow to tolerate mistakes. Their wages were based on the tonnage of cargo loaded or unloaded, and by some Victorian method that I never fully grasped, they knew to the last ounce what they had heaved or pushed and therefore, down to the last penny, exactly how much should be in their weekly pay-packets. They received extra money if they worked through rain or drizzle (an important distinction, as different rates applied for each. When does drizzle become rain? Discuss.), or handled excessively 'dirty' cargo such as coal or soya bean meal (there were also different rates for different types of dirt. Some dirt is dirtier than other dirt. There was clean dirt too, but isn't clean dirt not dirt at all?). Numbed by the complexity of this, I could make only a semi-educated guess as to what these wages might possibly amount.

Although constantly striving to err to their advantage, it didn't always work out. The margin of error was narrow, a generous overpayment unrecoverable and a serious underpayment suicidal. These gifted natural mathematicians collected their wages every Thursday afternoon, a day when I usually thought it prudent to make myself scarce in anticipation of the usual perceived shortfall in their pay packets. The furious short-changed brutes usually stormed the office, faces flushed with anger and alcohol, banging our office countertop with great horny fists, baying for blood, preferably mine.

If they didn't hunt me down on a Thursday, there was always Friday morning. I didn't mind so much as by then their fury had generally been tempered by hangovers. But Friday held other perils. As usual I showed up at whichever boat the dockers were working on, noting minor personnel changes in the workforce. Traversing the open deck of the ship was a necessary chore and particularly precarious. I had to keep a weather eye out for the powerful derrick that swung a sturdy iron hook back and forth between dock and ship. When it had deposited its load on land, the great grappling hook would fly through the air at an alarming rate of knots. And every once in a while the soundless hook was deliberately heaved in the direction of my cranium. I didn't always see it coming but was usually alerted by a last-minute shout from the derrick operator or a dogsbody on deck.

Admittedly, this gave me a sporting chance of survival but, nevertheless, I found this behaviour upsetting.

I mentioned it to my immediate superior.

'Those fuckers try to kill me every Friday.'

'Only a bit of fun. Get their wages right and they'll leave you alone.'

'Suppose they kill me?'

'They shout a warning, don't they?'

'I suppose they do. But it's touch and go at times.'

He narrowed his eyes and peered at me over the top of his glasses.

'Worry when they don't warn you.'

Maybe I wasn't cut out for this kind of work. Just as well I was sacked. At least I left with my head.

But collating dockers' wages had its perks. Each docker was equipped with a personal cardboard-backed wages book upon which was stamped his work number, name and nickname (important in a profession where jobs were handed down through families. There were many identical Joe Dohertys and many indistinguishable John Nashes), all that I needed to know about him for the purposes of making sure that the randomly calculated incorrect wages reached the right pocket.

Each docker who had been employed via the 'pool' (the rallying point for early morning hiring. Think the movie *On the Waterfront*) was conditioned to leave his book in a small wooden hut situated in an isolated corner beside a convenient railway line. It was my job to collect these small piles of books in order formally to identify those who were gainfully employed that day. The small hut contained a chair, a small table, a solitary naked light bulb and a two-bar electric fire. I had a key which I was allowed to keep at all times. It was, in all but name, my hut.

I was two months in the job before I realised the erotic possibilities of my stewardship of this humble bijou shed.

In an age when nobody had cars, never mind apartments, most courting was done in darkened alleyways. Persuading one's consort to undo the front buttons of her overcoat was regarded as a major breakthrough. That particular stream forded, it was henceforth every man for himself.

This method of getting at the female goods was a perfectly acceptable *modus operandi* during the summer months but non-productive and arduous in winter. The wind could fair whistle through thin garments up a back alley and no self-respecting, warm-blooded, God-fearing Catholic girl wanted her tit examined by an unacceptably icy hand.

This is where my two-bar electric fire came in.

As always, the correct approach was everything. Whenever I did manage to persuade a young lady to allow me to accompany her homewards, I would expound at length about the nature of the responsibilities my job entailed and the position of trust in which I was consequently placed. I would eventually get around to explaining to her that there was a place we could go with a roof and a two-bar electric fire. This soon weeded out the righteous and the hesitant. I discovered that the ones who agreed to explore the hut were the ones worth taking there. Those who resolutely refused were usually those whom others could confidently bring home to be introduced to mother.

However, I wanted more. I offered to hire the hut out to others for a fee.

I became a hut pimp.

It's not something I'm particularly proud of.

———

During the late fifties and early sixties, Derry was the perfect place in which to live if a person didn't want to amount to anything. It was also paradise for a ten-year-old.

I was born close to the docks where, as we have already gathered, I was destined to gain meaningful employment a few short years later, never far away from exotic guttural accents and hoarse foreign oaths shouted in the middle of the night by drunken sailors of all nationalities and hues. Derry was a lively and busy port then, despite our admirable Stormont government's seeming disapproval of all economic activity west of the River Bann. Merchantmen registered in Panama, Rio de Janeiro, Malmö and Copenhagen disgorged their crews onto the Derry quays at the onset of twilight, crews often consisting of surprisingly dusky men bent on wholeheartedly engaging in the predictable search for drink and women, and always in that strict order. More spectacular though were occasional nautical manoeuvres involving the entire NATO (North Atlantic Treaty Organization) fleet. The NATO navies descended upon Derry to take part in obscure exercises in the adjacent Atlantic which were designed better to aid the noble aim of world peace. When they weren't engaged thus, sailors from Britain, France, Sweden, Norway, Holland, Germany, Portugal, Denmark, America, Canada and the more minor nations, ran amok in the city. It was every man for himself and a wonderful sight.

Nothing inspired more than the sight of two thousand sailors trying to gain entry to the approximately six pubs that had the balls to serve them—living proof that the Devil is still firmly in control of every navy in the world.

These men could be awkward fuckers. Apart from the obvious language difficulties, many of these salts, particularly the Swedes, were constantly on the look-out for a rumble. This is how I learnt, as Darwin did before me, that it is possible to generalise, with a high degree of accuracy, when studying the behaviour of organisms belonging to closely related species or genera. For instance, one need never fear a Portuguese drunk, he is invariably gentle by nature, no matter how goaded, maddened or juiced. On the contrary, bitter experience taught one to steer clear of native English speakers in their cups. Only when we observe them pissed can we confirm that Brits, Americans and Canadians are genetically the same people (WASPs or no WASPs), whereas the Scandinavians, although equally violent when roused, tend to hold their liquor better.

I studied their different behavioural characteristics with the intense application of Darwin measuring the beaks of Galapagos finches. The French were pussies, fresh meat to most of the other nationalities. Ditto the Spaniards, bull-fighting or no.

I should have been frightened by this extreme drunkenness and constant street violence, but I wasn't. I roamed the streets at will, never feeling threatened in any way. Maybe I was just lucky.

I recall that I was on more-than-casual nodding terms with the hookers who congregated under a shop awning at the top of our street. The standard of hooker in those days was not high. Extreme ugliness seemed a requisite. Likewise the type of ultra-skinny legs that I will forever associate with the giving profession. Nor, unsurprisingly, did the girls waste much time on personal hygiene.

On Friday nights my mother would send me to the local chip shop with a large brown porcelain bowl. A fat woman would fill it to the brim with stubby chips and a handily-sized tea-cloth was draped over the top to retain essential heat. I usually exchanged words of greeting with the hookers on my way home. They were friendly and I liked them. I would often offer them a chip or two, which they appreciated greatly. Anything that would warm them up a little was welcome, and they also seemed to like talking to people who didn't want to leap on their bones.

Hookers wear the same light clothes in winter as they do in summer, for obvious reasons. I encouraged them to dip into the bowl. It didn't occur to me then to speculate as to where their hands might recently have been. This spontaneous act of generosity sometimes led to a noticeable shortfall when the chips were ladled out by my mother. My mother was understanding about the absent chips, but even then I thought to myself that it is the rare child of whom his mother has to enquire, 'Have you been feeding those prostitutes again?'

Down on Derry docks was an exciting place to be young. I found it difficult to sleep unless I heard a girl scream, the crash of a bottle in the street, or the gruff rasp of alien expletives.

I also had a bicycle, and a boy with a bicycle could earn himself a little pocket money by making himself available during daylight hours when the ships were in port and the sailors busy onboard performing various semi-nautical tasks which usually involved sluicing down the decks or heaving large vats of putrefying garbage overboard. On any given day, there were a number of us urchins on duty. Here again we applied intuitive sociological insights pragmatically arrived at by hours of participant observation.

In short, there was no point in hanging around British, Swedish, Portuguese or German vessels. Whatever other noble national traits they shared, being liberal with their loose change wasn't one of them.

The Yanks were the big spenders. Their ships even smelled different. It was a peculiar odour, like no other. I have rarely come a whiff like it since. It is the smell of excess and waste—even the rotten garbage they tipped over the side smelled exotic when it mingled with salt water. It wasn't like the stuff we had in our bins at home. I realised early that there was such a thing as a better class of garbage.

We performed a public service. If perchance a Yank lusted after a bar of local chocolate (and some of them did indeed prefer Cadbury's Wholenut to their Hershey Bars. I never understood why. As far as I was concerned, there was no contest), a pint of fresh milk, a dozen farmyard eggs, or even a whole box of chocolates as a gift for his girl that night, we were ready.

At first the sailors trusted us with only smallish sums until we lulled them into a false sense of security by always showing up with the goods requested and offering to return any small change that materialised as a result of the transaction. As soon as they trusted us enough to buy something expensive that involved throwing a pound note (!) to one of us, that boy (or throwee) was never seen again. It was the way of the world.

The Yanks didn't seem to mind. They understood that theft is an essential component of a capitalist-driven democracy. Sailors of other nationalities tended to brand us as petty thieves. The Americans regarded us as entrepreneurs and blamed themselves for trusting us. They knew more about the global marketplace than the others.

But one of us was smarter than the rest. His name was Dickie. A Bicycle Boy too, Dickie travelled nowhere without his pet Alsatian pup. It was a lovable cur, much admired by sailors of many nationalities, who, of course, were forbidden pets on board warships. One could understand such a rule. But there was one flaxen-haired American pet-lover who was not to be denied. He wanted to own the pup. In due course, a deal was done.

The night before his ship was due to sail (to Philadelphia, as I recall) a considerable amount of money changed hands and the pup was smuggled onboard, the plan being that the sailor would keep the animal under wraps until the ship crossed the Atlantic. It was eminently doable. The pup was placid by nature.

However, a rider was attached to the verbal contract between dog-seller and sailor. The sailor should've known better.

As the boat sailed on the eight-a.m. high tide, most of the city was asleep (remember this is Derry, where dawn breaks at midday). It was agreed that the sailor would sneak the dog on deck to be seen one more time by its previous owner, who, sentimental soul that he was, naturally wanted to wish the pooch God speed.

We thieving messenger boys made it our business to present ourselves when the convoy set sail, leaning on our rusting bikes as the might of Uncle Sam's fleet churned the surf and prepared to chug Stateside.

Our eyes were trained on the poop deck of the pup ship. Sure enough, the innocent sailor was true to his word. He dutifully appeared at the stern, where he couldn't be seen from any other part of the ship, and hoisted a small wriggling dog above his head. He urged a paw to wave goodbye to its previous owner.

From behind me came the unexpected trill of two shrill whistles from a human throat. When these piercing sounds hit the dog's well-trained ears, it squirmed from its new master's grasp, launched itself over the side of the boat and hit the water, doing the breast-stroke. The amphibian struck out strongly for shore.

In a matter of minutes, the dripping dog was again happily trotting behind the bicycle of its devoted owner.

Neither of them considered a backward, seaward glance towards the forlorn white-hatted figure steaming towards America alone.

It was dog-eat-dog down those docks.

————

Otherwise, at this time Derry was a grey, defeated city, populated by many lively and vital souls who correctly sensed that nobody gave a fuck about them. Of course, like anywhere else, we had our fair share of grandstanders, crooks and gombeen men, but I often wondered, and still do, how a deeply flawed place like Northern Ireland could ever hope to thrive and prosper whilst disregarding its second largest city and so undervaluing the many vibrant and talented people who lived there. A deep sense of discontentment hung in the air like a noxious vapour. The majority of the citizens of Derry felt somehow stateless. There are perfectly valid historical reasons why they felt that way but that didn't make the people feel any better.

In truth, the government of Northern Ireland in the fifties and sixties was enthusiastically engaged in making sure that the city withered economically and, I'm sure, would've heaved a sigh of relief had it slipped off the map and slid beneath the Atlantic.

Being born a Catholic in Derry meant being introduced to the concept of less-than-full citizenship. I didn't feel it all that much at the time. It sneaks up late but eventually bites deep. Nor did schooldays seem in any way unduly strained. However, I do remember thinking that nobody ever explained anything to me. Nor did I think to ask questions. It didn't seem polite. Curiosity wasn't encouraged.

Of course, I was told more than I strictly needed to know about the operation of Boyle's Law and the advisability of the limited use of onomatopoeia, but about why I was studying and which goals I was striving to achieve, nothing. We were told that 'O' Levels were good things to pass but never why.

I marvel now that I was so incredibly naïve. I knew no better.

I didn't find out until I was thirty that I could have gone to university had I passed my 'A' Levels. Nobody told me what I needed to know when it mattered that I knew.

We weren't destined to have careers. I do, however, remember a visit from one strange dishevelled person whom our teacher breathlessly explained was a representative from the 'Civil Service.' He must have been given the wrong address. He stumbled into our classroom one winter afternoon reeking heavily of whiskey and cigarette smoke. He wore an old-fashioned three-piece dark suit and carried with him a number of loose cardboard files which he promptly dropped, scattering pieces of A4 paper under the front two desks.

As the small inhabitants of the desks helpfully scrambled to retrieve the papers, the Civil Service grouch snapped them out of their hands as if they contained the launch codes for inter-continental missiles. When composed and propped up against a worn lectern that had been wheeled out for his benefit, he extolled the virtues of a career in lower clerkdom. He waffled earnestly about pension schemes, not something that greatly concerns twelve-year-old boys. All that was required was that we sit some form of Civil Service entrance examination. None us of considered it for a moment. I suppose we retained a collective pre-ternatural folk suspicion of recruiters who didn't seem to like us but were nevertheless charged with operating a system that required worker bees. Whatever our other shortcomings, we had a healthy inherited dis-respect for the King's Shilling.

Our teachers were the Irish Christian Brothers and I suppose we mattered to them as potential foot-soldiers in the good fight against evil and Communism to come, but in the meantime they just worked out on us and honed their interrogation skills. And I must have seen and failed to respond to *Mise Éire* a thousand times, so regularly did they herd us into the main assembly hall to watch the film. I remember thinking the music was quite nice but, even then, I sensed I was watch-ing something that wouldn't do me much good if I absorbed it fully. I was also distrustful about the way the Christian Brothers studied us closely as we watched the film, as if intent on identifying those who were moved by the movie. Raw material for the good fight. Maybe they could brainwash those later. The sentimental ones—the needy ones—the fools.

And there were those who bought the whole package. Many of my school friends were quite taken by the mood of the movie, sitting bolt upright and glassy eyed until the last frame clicked away. It's surprising how many of them subsequently ended up in cages during the Troubles that were to follow. Sometimes it pays to be a film critic.

But, so what if I'd been told that I could have gone to university if I'd passed my 'A' Levels. Six months before I was due to sit my 11+, I collapsed in primary school during religious instruction imparted by a bald priest with an orange head. His name was Father Rooney. The last thing I remember before the classroom tipped over was explanatory talk of the provenance and significance of scapulars, relics and other forms of traditional white man's juju.

I regained consciousness in the back seat of his car. There seemed no risk involved in getting into a car with a priest in those days. He tossed a soft sweet over his shoulder and drove me home. An impatient doctor was summoned and I spent the next six months in bed. I didn't feel particularly ill and, indeed, felt relatively well, apart from the fact that I couldn't walk when I managed periodically to struggle to my feet.

I was never told what was wrong with me, of course. I still don't know. 'Some kind of physical breakdown,' my mother used to mutter when I enquired about it in later years. People didn't give much away in those days.

One of my teachers, the late Hugh Kelly, was a fine man with advanced ideas for the time and, instead of letting me rot in bed during the run-up to the 11+, decided to call to my home every now and again, keeping me up to date with class work.

I welcomed the distraction and embarked upon a programme of relentless study. I also, having nothing but time to kill, read all the books that my father kept on top of his wardrobe, everything from *Moby Dick* to *The Martian Chronicles*.

When the time came to sit my 11+, I was deemed fit and ready.

As far as I knew, overcoming this milestone meant that I would be forced to attend the formidable St Columb's College, a grammar school with a fearsome reputation. I knew of this place because my two elder brothers had attended when they were my age. They didn't last long. Before the end of their first terms, both were forced to leave, or more accurately, retire hurt. My oldest brother Johnny, as a consequence of losing an eye courtesy of a shard of stone cast up by a pneumatic street drill, and Charlie, who suffered a debilitating concussion as a result of a kick to the head administered during a school football match.

I, therefore, associated St Columb's College with physical injury, pain and possible facial disfigurement. It wasn't for me.

I ended up being educated by the Christian Brothers. Lay teachers made up the numbers. One indication of the quality of the education provided was that although taught by a future Nobel prize winner and by a man now regarded as Ireland's greatest living playwright, I still managed to learn nothing.

The former, John Hume, seemed to spend most of his time staring dreamily out of the window. Not that I minded, that was how I passed most of my days too.

The latter, Brian Friel, then faintly dislikeable, was the kind of teacher who didn't seem to have much time for children. This was clearly not the profession for him. His nickname was Scobie.

———

The mood in the Derry of the fifties was that of an independent statelet—Monaco but without the money.

We grew up with a sense of alienation. We didn't know who we were or what we belonged to. We were neither Irish nor British. Northern Ireland meant nothing to us.

Ulster was for other people who didn't want us about the place. We belonged only to the street in which we lived. Nobody seemed to like or to pay much attention to us. We were disenfranchised, discriminated against and herded into certain voting wards to prevent a break in Unionist political hegemony. Ulster was a nasty piece of work. No wonder the genie burst from the bottle and ignited the Troubles.

It was always only a matter of time.

There was no pressure to succeed in life because it was taken as given that the odds were against us. Life with the Christian Brothers effectively instilled in me a lifelong abhorrence of any form of group activity. I left school to join the dole queue where I languished happily for more than two years. It was no bad life at the time. There is no stigma attached to being unemployed if all one's mates are idle too.

And, anyway, I had a guitar to keep me busy. I practised incessantly, driving my father to such despair that he often hurled the *Daily Express* at me in fury. A key constituent of my (or any) practice regime involved playing the same musical phrase over and over. Some decent men can only take so much of that. He didn't know what a narrow escape he'd had. My original plan to procure a plastic alto saxophone had run afoul due to lack of capital. I wanted to play jazz, just like my brother Johnny. He had introduced me to the trombone but, not being the tallest or most supple of youths, my arm was too short to stretch to the vital B Natural position, nestling at the far end of the slide. I subsequently con-templated the trumpet but my heart was lost when I spotted the sax in the window of Deery's Music shop. It was ivory white and glistened bravely in the weak sun. Most saxophones I'd seen before were brassy looking things, cold and forbidding, but this was different. We must remember that the late fifties was a time when plastic was considered avant-garde. And that's what I liked about it. The fact that Roland Kirk played one just like it clinched matters for me. I regarded myself as a 'jazzer', wholly influenced by the heads who infested our house. Their numbers had grown exponentially when word circulated that my mother was willing to feed them.

Whilst normal individuals of my particular vintage were listening to guitar groups like The Shadows, I was poring over recordings by Stan Kenton, Gerry Mulligan and Cannonball Adderley.

I wasn't interested in playing 'Apache' by The Shadows. No, more interested in another Indian tribe, I wanted to play 'Cherokee' by Charlie Parker.

Other musical influences played a part. Whilst still in the clutches of the Christian Brothers I had applied to join the choir of St Eugene's Cathedral, partly because I'd heard they went off to the seaside on bus excursions each summer and were given free buns and lemonade. I also liked the music I heard in chapel on a Sunday when not distracted by my usual method of passing the time, which chiefly involved scanning the congregation in the hope of finding somebody with a really big nose, or, alternatively, counting the number of men wearing bad wigs. The worst of the wigs seemed to spike viciously just above the collar and the colour of the ersatz hair never seemed to even vaguely match that of the wearer's natural sideburns.

No vague notion of religion or faith had anything to do with my attendance at mass on a Sunday—the Brothers, by scrupulous example, had seen to it that I was never again to waste time or precious energy on matters even remotely theological, something for which I will always remain thankful.

Sunday morning also taught me how to eat when I wasn't hungry. This skill came in handy later on the road when I always felt it prudent to consume food long past the departure of appetite, on the principle that one never knew when one might eat again. The camel understands this well, water-wise.

I lived quite near our local place of worship and could comfortably languish in bed until at least 11.30, confident that I would make midday

Mass with minutes to spare and breakfast aboard. I usually sat down to a huge fried breakfast at 11.45.

I would return from midday mass approximately one hour later, to be confronted by a four-course dinner of gargantuan proportions. There was never any question of dining later. Breakfast was served in the morning (which, of course, lasted until noon), lunch at 12.45 p.m. on the dot. That's the way things had always been and would remain so.

The organist and choirmaster was a gruff but cultured German, a certain Herr Haan, a lachrymose German national who'd somehow managed to dodge the rise of National Socialism and ended up in Derry (insert your own joke here).

Haan ran a tight, grim ship but played wonderfully. The great pipe organ that rose behind us was surely constructed solely for the purpose of facilitating the glory of Bach's Mass in B Minor. I habitually sat in a state of near ecstasy watching Haan's bony but elegant fingers skitter across the keyboards rendering a faultless 'Jesu, Joy of Man's Desiring', deeply moved by its beauty, simplicity, neatness and (as I now know but didn't then) mathematical structure.

I also learnt to sight-read music for voice, a facility that gradually deserted me as I matured, although I have no doubt that whatever rudimentary ear for music I subsequently enjoyed was enhanced by the discipline involved.

I was particularly happy when the Bishop rode into town. He had a signature tune which we choirboys particularly enjoyed belting out. It was a hearty, optimistic ditty called '*Ecce Sacerdos*', lustily rendered when the considerable bulk of His Purpleness hoved into view at the back of the Church on über days like Easter Sunday or Christmas.

It was important that this tune kicked off at the precise moment of his appearance before the multitudes. Problem was, it was impossible to see him enter the building from where we sat, perched as we were directly above the entrance to the cathedral. To complicate matters further, the positioning of the organ dictated that Haan necessarily had his back to the altar whilst at the keyboard. In order to see what was going on, he'd had the great structure kitted out with a set of impressive wing mirrors through which he could spot his cues. No cue was more important than that which initiated the Bishop's Coming-In-The-Door tune. To this end, one of the lowlier priests was assigned to signal Haan when the Bishop's entry was imminent. The corpulent prelate would then strut his way regally down the nave, providing a fleeting opportunity for the grubby fingers of the lumpen proletariat almost to touch the hem of his raiment. Close, but no cigar.

As we lashed out the Bishop's tune to an undulating, pious mob I realised that the proceedings I was witnessing weren't driven by any form of meaningful spirituality—this was something else.

Something more familiar.

This was show business.

This was my personal epiphany. All boys should join church choirs. That way, if they remain alert, they see how things work behind the scenes, invaluable training for life in a cruel world ahead.

And, once I realised that the clergy were in the entertainment business, everything slotted into place and made sense. Religion was there to make us feel good. It was medicine, insurance against thought.

I have never given it another moment's consideration...

———

The plastic alto saxophone cost a prohibitive £70, an unimaginable sum to someone who, as I did, subsisted on a meagre dole handout of £4 a week, three-and-a-half of which were handed in at home (also known as the 3.10 to You Ma. Think pre-decimal). I'd have to settle for a less expensive instrument.

One of the heads who nested in our kitchen was a jazz guitar player from Dublin called Sean Reilly who had procured sporadic employment with a local outfit. He was an elegant if fussily turned-out individual with a theatrical moustache and a deep, booming voice. A dandy and unrepentant silver-tongued rogue, he was hard to resist and succeeded in charming my mother to the extent that he was invited to move in as a lodger. He was a likeable, unprincipled though harmless rake, tiny in stature, tidy of habit and pleasant of expression. I observed him closely when he came to live with us. He revealed that he was descended from 'show' people, and had travelled with his parents with the old 'fit-ups' (travelling theatre and variety shows that had flourished in Ireland for centuries until their eventual demise in the fifties, and I'm sure one or two of them carried on even after that). The fit-ups died slowly and without much fuss, in much the same way as the circus slowly expires today.

He permitted me to hold his guitar and demonstrated rudimentary chord shapes. At that time there were traditionally two kinds of guitar player, rhythm or lead. Reilly was definitely a chord man. Chord men were a dying breed. The rhythmic chop of the strummed guitar was once an essential element of any small band's rhythm section. And big bands too, as witnessed by the faint ker-ching of Freddie Green's guitar disciplining the mighty roar of the Count Basie Band. Harbouring ambitions to be a rhythm guitarist was a somewhat donnish calling, attractive only to those who treasured the minutiae of life—I wasn't aware at the time that I was skirting the territory of the nerd.

In more recent years, of course, with the rise of guitar groups like The Shadows and later The Beatles, rhythm guitarists found themselves thrust into the limelight. But they still seemed a little odd, like trainspotters or bird-watchers, often ignored and sometimes castigated, if not downright pitied. General opinion seemed to brand them as not accomplished enough to be lead guitarists, in much the same way as Christian Brothers were thought of as failed priests. Anyway, what did I care? I was living in the past anyway. I'd never harboured ambitions to be a lead guitarist.

Those who played lead guitar seemed somehow vulgar to me, show boaters who craved attention. Deep down, I still feel that way today, illogical though it may seem in a world full of axe heroes who live only to thrust their bollocks at an audience.

Reilly promised to teach me more if I was keen. I subsequently purchased an acoustic Hofner guitar, £2 down and thirteen shillings a month, just within my budget. I regarded it as a thing of beauty.

I applied myself with vigour, cooped up in my bedroom for hours each day, attempting to master awkward chord shapes until the tips of the fingers on my left hand were raw. Reilly gave me a small red book containing the handwritten chord progressions of standard ballads, old chestnuts like 'All The Things You Are,' 'Sweet Georgia Brown', 'I Got Rhythm' and 'Laura.' These were hopelessly advanced for me, of course, but I didn't know that. Sometimes it's better not to know that one is attempting something beyond one's capabilities. O'Reilly encouraged me greatly, which is more than could be said for those whom I met during my weekly visit to the only guitar display room in town, in a music shop called Derryvision.

Every Saturday afternoon, budding guitarists would gather in the music showroom, each casually lifting a guitar and playing his party piece for the benefit of gawking onlookers. It was a teenage reassurance ritual, a chance to show off and perhaps filch tips from other players. It was also the only opportunity many of us ever had to play guitar through a real amplifier.

Most of the neophytes churned out standard guitar riffs from pop songs of the day—a Shadows' instrumental called 'Foot-tapper' was particularly abused on a regular basis—the 'Stairway to Heaven' of its time.

My hard-learned chords, were, however, received with bouts of general tittering. I couldn't understand this and often felt hurt. I was that worst of things, a teenager playing old people's music.

Luckily, I soon found a kindred spirit. Pat was a loner too, a closet jazzer floundering in a world of pop fans. He played trumpet and modelled himself on Miles Davis. There is an obsequious album cover that depicts Miles in full-length silhouette. Never an orthodox trumpeter, it seemed appropriate that when Miles adopted the playing position, his body formed an unnatural 'S' shape, pelvis thrust out, back hunched, trumpet protruding from mouth at a unnatural angle. When Pat lifted a trumpet from the display stand, his body immediately contorted into that of Miles' hunched silhouette, the metamorphosis complete.

We subsequently became close friends and retreated often to the tiny 'good' front room of his parents' miniscule house where we smoked heavily and listened reverentially to Miles' 'Sketches of Spain', 'Porgy and Bess', and 'Milestones.' But it didn't stop there. Mono-thumbed guitarist Wes Montgomery, Charlie Parker, and grunting pianist Errol Gardner were there with us too.

We were in paradise, cocooned from the horrible world of Cliff Richard, Tommy Steele and Frank Ifield. Elvis was an interesting freak but irrelevant to us. Chuck Berry was a curio too, oddly literate but somehow cold-blooded and detached. Although imperfectly aware of it, we were seeking quality, nothing cosmetic detained us.

And I suppose, if the truth be told, we felt a cut above the common-weal, not necessarily a bad thing if the commonweal was keen on circus turns like Wee Willie Harris and Tommy Quickly.

In short, we were pompous little fuckers. But better to be pompous seventeen-year-old little fuckers with time on our side and a sporting chance of growing out of it.

8

Billy Brown and I crept carefully down the steep stone steps out-side the Abbotsford Hotel and made our way unsteadily across the street to where the band wagon was parked. I suppose the vehicle could more accurately be described as a coach, custom-built in Dundalk by an inspired man who led the field in the construction of death-traps for Irish showbands with a taste for conspicuous consumption. Somewhat smaller in scale than a conventional commercial bus, it had an arrogant, fifties look about it. It was garish, with strong show-business lines. These band coaches always reminded me of giant Dodgem cars, and, in many respects, their function was similar. Unfortunately, our particular model was a shade top-heavy. It didn't handle well and was dangerously predictable at anything over fifty miles an hour. And awkward as fuck on even the most gentle of bends. I'm sure we would have been killed long ago if our driver had been a normal person.

His name was Harpo. He had a proper name but preferred not to use it. That made three of us from the North. Only one more Nordie to come. As I approached now, I could see Harpo slumped in the driver's seat, his face one inch from a magazine that doubtless featured lewd acts by consenting adults. Harpo's hair looked like a fright-wig, fuzzy curls framing a face straight from the pages of *Oliver Twist*, suspicious eyes, thin mouth and prominent chin. Shallow, shifty and lazy, he was perfect for us. Fearless to the point of madness, he only fully came to life when we needed to get from A to B quickly. He loved being late for a gig. It gave him an excuse to take risks that we wouldn't normally tolerate. We disliked him for it and feared he'd kill us all eventually.

The exterior of the coach was particularly filthy today. Harpo's cleansing hand had obviously not been applied since last weekend when those arse-baring, egg-throwing bastards had disturbed us outside Limerick. It was a band called the 'Kerry Blues'. I knew of them because I had once seen a poster for one of their gigs. Around the perimeter of this poster were seven circular photographs of dogs (presumably belonging to the Kerry Blue breed). Underneath the likeness of each dog was the name of one of the members of the band. I'd never understood the point of that. It just seemed, well, odd—a showband thing.

Another showband 'thing' that puzzled some Nordies was the tendency to incorporate the band's place of origin in the official name of the band. Certain individuals in the Brown and O'Brien band tended to make fun of this. Not me, though. During tours of Irish clubs in England, I had come to understand the power of openly declaring one's point of origin for the purpose of attracting homesick ex-pats, so that these wretches could gaze winsomely upon men in shiny suits who were just like themselves—except better. I had been in the Irish Trenches in England.

I was that soldier.

It was important that these bands be placed in the great geographical scheme of things. There was Joe Dolan and the Drifters, Mullingar. The Royal Showband, Waterford, The Dixielanders, Cork, The Black Aces, Kilkenny. Even the minnows did it. I once spotted the obscurely sited Barrow Boys, Graiguenamanagh.

And when you think about it, it is distinctly odd. After all, it would be rare to find a poster in England advertising The Who, Dagenham, or the Animals, Newcastle. But then, of course, we had The Beatles, Liverpool. All bets are off then, even though all but Ringo were Liverpool-Irish.

Anyway, a long-standing tradition between showbands on the road decreed that when one crossed the path of another in isolated terrain far from home there would be a wholesome egg-fight.

We were somewhere outside Limerick, I believe, when we first spotted the opening gambit of bared arses pressed against the windows of a recklessly overtaking coach.

Harpo clumsily swung his unwieldy charge to the side of the road and braked abruptly. We let the interlopers proceed, secure in the knowledge that the Kerry Blues would be further down the road waiting round the next convenient bend, bare-arsed and armed with poultry produce (bags of flour sometimes too).

When we got going again, they were precisely where we expected them to be. Five of them stood in the middle of the road holding eggs menacingly aloft, trousers hugging their ankles, arses to the wind.

I'd never understood the significance of a bared arse as an integral component of the egg-fight ritual. Maybe something vaguely Celtic. It's an avenue probably best left unexplored.

Anyway, confronted by this, we were expected to stop, dismount, drop our trousers and throw foodstuffs too—a bonding ritual—innocent fun.

But we didn't like innocent fun. It didn't appeal to us. We felt we had moved on.

Harpo knew what he had to do. He gunned the engine and headed straight for them. Spooked, the egg-wielders dived for the ditch.

The Kerry Blues should have known we were anti-social. Surely word had spread by now. We were strangely proud of our sullied reputation.

———

Harpo was alone in the coach. We were early for the call. I peered through a grimy window and surveyed the detritus scattered on the floor of the vehicle and strewn across the roomy, comfortable seats that lined the once-plush interior. A comprehensive collection of empty wine, beer and spirit bottles had washed its way into a vacant nook, competing with the decaying remains of forgotten fish suppers. All around lay the remnants of squashed chips and sodden shards of hamburger bun. I figured it was only a matter of time before we would have to deal with the scuttling and slithering of a variety of vermin.

Also scattered about the floor were sundry items of personal clothing, including disembodied trousers, isolated samples of female trophy underwear, loose playing cards, cigarette ends, dubious magazines, torn newspapers, mangled paperbacks, and a miner's helmet (complete with functioning light).

All in all, a pig-sty.

But it was home.

This was where we spent the greater part of our time.

The miner's helmet was mine. I'd picked it up in a junk shop in London—ideal for reading in the van after dark. Harpo couldn't drive if the interior lights were in use, something to do with refraction.

The coach was parked at the pick-up spot, just outside our management's office on the sunny side of Harcourt Street. We had a strained relationship with the people who ran us and looked after our affairs, the inevitable result of our deeply held belief that they did not have our best interests at heart and were concerned only with what they could steal from us, by far the healthiest attitude to adopt when dealing with people who professed to know better than we did.

We foot soldiers generally regarded the managers of showbands as tiresome con men, forever on the 'stroke.' (Definition: a 'stroke' is an underhand action or deed that succeeds in fucking up the person being stroked whilst at the same time relieving him of sizeable amounts of money.)

The generally criminal nature of managerial talent stemmed largely from the nature of the business itself. Those who eagerly peddled flawed product were, by necessity, generally flawed themselves. The showband phenomenon had mushroomed so unexpectedly in the early sixties that its ephemeral though highly lucrative nature attracted the nasty, brutish and unscrupulous who, in another era, would have been carnival barkers, bookies' runners, pimps (hello?) or gombeen men. Experience had taught us to be extremely wary of the breed and we behaved accordingly, having as little to do with them as possible. Managers were, however, a necessary evil. They took care of troublesome minor matters and furnished us with a list of gigs every month. I liked having my movements planned. It removed the tedium of having to make decisions.

A screech of brakes almost resulted in the hearts within our chests turning crossways. We were standing near the middle of the road beside the coach and instinctively leapt smartly aside to avoid the hastily-halted vehicle. Turned out it was friendly fire, a gleaming red Mercedes saloon, piloted by a cheery tousle-headed blond youth with prominent white teeth, a longish nose and a set of blue eyes that twinkled with mischief. He brayed a guttural but infectious laugh as he leaned out of the driver's window and rested his head playfully on the crook of his elbow.

'Caught yez on the hop there, ya baaastards!'

It was Mike O'Brien, the other half of the Brown and O'Brien singing partnership.

I was surprised to see him. He didn't usually travel in the coach with the rest of us. Nor, as it turned out, did he plan to do so today. Probably just passing through. We wouldn't normally have spotted him until we arrived at whatever gig we were playing and even then, never until it was almost time to go on stage. Not that there was anything wrong with that, as far as I was concerned. Others in the band didn't much care for this *modus operandi* but I understood.

O'Brien thought it important to act like a star. This meant not being seen tumbling dishevelled from a van outside some mangy dance hall and hanging about chatting listlessly to grubby locals whilst the roadies carried in the gear. Too ordinary and demeaning. The game was about appearing 'big'. This meant not being seen or heard anywhere near the dance hall whilst the first punters were straggling in at the start of the night. This meant not being seen until he burst upon the stage in all his primped glory and launched into what he referred to as his 'shapes.'

All lead singers worth the name had their defining 'shapes', an individually crafted series of physical movements (they could be either subtle or restrained. There were no rules) that shaped their persona on stage. Brendan Bowyer has his ersatz Elvis schtick diluted by the suspicion that he would otherwise have made an efficient priest, Dickie Rock the same, only mean, anaemic, wiry, ruthless but decidedly not seminary material; Joe Dolan, the shy country bumpkin come good who would occasionally burst into high-pitched wails and launch himself into transports of testosterone-driven show-business-generated ecstasy; Larry Cunningham with the syrupy voice, looking pleadingly skywards as he melted women's hearts with his primeval bullfrog croak; Eileen Reid in her optimistically white wedding dress, surrounded by the uniformed members of an unspecified army (The Cadets to you), Big Tom, the lumbering Neanderthal, mother-loving gentle giant seemingly bemused at being on stage at all, therefore garnering the sympathy of every sad-sack and woman in the hall, right down to Wee Mick the Hootenanny Dwarf, walking the plank for the punters. There was room for everybody while it lasted.

O'Brien trod a fine line in that his 'shapes' were decidedly effeminate if not downright homosexual. Not that he was what we would nowadays categorise as 'gay'. No, not him.

Playing the gay card on stage was acceptable in cities but a finely gauged risk in front of a mob of an agricultural bent, who tended to take this depiction of sexual aberration a tad more seriously. By which I mean that women loved it and the men took the dimmer view.

I liked Mike O'Brien for his cheerful hedonism. He and Brown were odd bedfellows. They had absolutely nothing in common except a shared ambition to fuck all the women in the world. Otherwise, they didn't connect or relate to each other in any meaningful way.

O'Brien was also known in the business as a 'punter's man' i.e. someone who could effortlessly relate to the commonweal. Billy could have done the same if he'd felt so inclined. He usually chose not to.

O'Brien was an uncomplicated, happy-go-lucky, pop-crazy, handsome middle-class Dublin boy who just wanted to be famous, make loads of money and be lusted after by women. He was shallow, feckless and vain. I wanted to be just like him.

Brown, a shade optimistically perhaps, regarded himself as more of an artist than entertainer. He was in the wrong business. Although by no means averse to sins of the flesh, he was of a more serious nature. There was a Northern-Irish darkness about him that I had seen in others of the tribe, a sense of foreboding and impending doom that often marks the Ulster Scot. The ghost of John Calvin stalked the Six Counties and haunted the sons thereof. Who knew what demons inhabited Billy Brown's skull.

This was why O'Brien was in the band, to sell it on stage. Unlike Brown, O'Brien was happy every night. Billy's job was to provide the musical bricks. O'Brien was the bricklayer.

'What time's the call?' O'Brien asked.

'Oh, not until three,' I said. 'We're early.'

O'Brien squinted up at Billy, who was rather pointedly staring into the middle distance. I often wished he would try a bit harder with O'Brien. If only for the sake of politeness.

'Wanna travel down with me, head?' offered the genial O'Brien.

'What time you leaving?' Billy replied, displaying scant interest.

'Fiveish.'

'Nah, too much time to kill. I'll go in the van with the lads.'

There was a patent awkwardness between them that was hard to quantify.

Miserable fucker, I thought. It wouldn't have hurt Billy to have acted even slightly friendly towards O'Brien.

O'Brien nodded, nonplussed, and gunned the motor. As he sped away, he shot us a wide grin. Ever the cheery.

'See ya there. Onwards and upwards!'

We watched him disappear into traffic snaking round St Stephen's Green. Edging onto the footpath to the door of the coach, we stepped up into the vehicle and sidled past the engrossed Harpo. I peeked over his shoulder at his specialist reading material. It was as I thought. A naked Asian woman was being severely pressed on both sides by an equally naked though, admittedly, turbaned Indian and a similarly unclothed but bare-headed black man.

'What's going on there?' I idly enquired.

Harpo didn't look up.

'It's a sandwich,' he grunted.

Well, yes.

Billy and I settled into two spacious but filthy airplane seats and stared straight ahead in the comfort of an easy silence.

The others would be along soon.

9

Eddie seemed disconsolate as we neared the van after our pharmaceutical interlude. The heap was clumsily parked outside the pub where the rest of them were waiting, doubtless enjoying pints of local stout.

He dug his hands deep into the pockets of his overcoat and stared at the uneven pavement ahead.

'I don't think we should do that again,' he muttered. 'It doesn't feel right.'

'Of course, it doesn't,' I replied. 'That's the fun of it.'

'That charver's bound to get into trouble when her boss gets back. It's just not right. She was nice to us.'

'Consider it part of her ongoing education,' sez I. 'So what if the boss gives her the bollocking of her life when she tells him about us? It's one of the hazards of working in premises that stock artificial stimulants. People like you and I will occasionally walk in the front door and complicate her life. She'll come out the other end a wiser and better person. Let her fondly remember us as harbingers of modern-day mores. It'll teach her not to judge by appearances. Now, that's a good thing.'

Bearing our hard-won brown paper bags (we had already discarded the Lucozade etc. in a convenient bin) Eddie and I pushed our way through the scabrous exterior doors of the dingy pub and sonared our way through the gloom.

This pub was old. I could smell at least two hundred years' worth of not much happening. A solitary man of gnarled and crumpled mien sat perched like an abandoned marionette on a high stool. He seemed mechanically fastened to the bar counter. A wisp of smoke drifting from the bowl of his pipe betrayed the only evidence that this figure was a functioning human being. Artfully unshaven, he wore a cap that looked as if it had been on his head since Mafeking Night. He reminded me of my Uncle Manny, then ensconced in a small farmhouse clinging to the side of a barren hill in Donegal.

Manny never removed his cap either, not even when summoned by surgeons to undergo a minor operation. He lay on his hospital bed, cap resolutely still on head. The hospital staff had encountered his type before and permitted the headgear to remain on his skull until an anaesthetic had been administered. The mouldy cap was then removed. Successful surgery was duly performed and he was wheeled back to the ward in order to recuperate. The cap was repositioned on his head when it looked as if he was about to regain consciousness. To his dying day he believed that he had undergone a gall-bladder operation with his cap on. He was often bought drinks on the strength of this claim. Damn the begrudgers, he would say.

Manny lived in a thatched house and, at the age of thirty-five sustained a minor injury to his hip in the act of climbing onto the roof to replace the thatch. He resolved not to recover and, strategically seated beside the settle bed, stared at the turf fire for the remaining fifty-five years of his life. There are those in this world who might baulk at the prospect of gazing idly at a turf fire for more than half a century but he accomplished it with consummate ease, and would have continued for much longer but for the intervention of the Grim Reaper.

Once he had chosen the appropriate chair, the rest was simple. By his right hand stood a two-foot-tall ashtray ready to accommodate the ash that unavoidably accrued from the sixty untipped Players cigarettes that he smoked daily. By his left hand side panted a dog, usually a border collie of dubious provenance. Manny went through approximately seven dogs during the course of his self-imposed invalidity. They were all called 'Gyp.' Not Gyp 1 or Gyp 2, just Gyp. When one Gyp died, a younger Gyp quietly took its place. Manny never seemed to mind or, indeed, to notice the difference. The serial Gyps were there to have their ears fondled on demand—almost like hookers. No tearing after sheep was required, no rounding up of cattle in foul weather, and no brief to bark at strangers who came to the door. None of that. The dogs spent their lives by Manny's side and stared at the fire too.

Happy dogs, their only duty was just to be there when he occasionally decided to pat them on the head and softly whisper, 'There, boy.'

He seldom spoke. Nobody knew what was going on in his head.

There was certainly evidence that he conducted inward conversations with people whose identity he never revealed. These conversations would invariably contain an element of mystery as he would occasionally smile broadly and say, 'Now you're talking, boy!' indicating that whatever was going on in his head had a cast of at least two.

He seemed to read the papers daily until he was observed holding the *Sunday Independent* upside down two days in a row.

Manny's diet consisted solely of bread, boiled potatoes and sour buttermilk. No other vegetable, item of salad or portion of fruit ever passed his lips, nor did cornflakes, muesli, protein, or fibre of any kind. The fact that he lived to be ninety years old may have had something to do with the other vital component of his diet. The Water of Life. He was in the habit of drinking a bottle of whiskey a day.

I once suggested to him that this could be construed as heavy drinking. He disagreed, pointing out that a conventional bottle's worth drunk intermittently over twenty-four hours, including frequent sips in bed, could hardly be described as drinking at all. I felt inclined to agree.

He wore a night-cap in bed and preferred a porcelain hot water-bottle.

But I digress.

I approached the old man sitting at the bar. He fixed a gimlet eye on me and slowly removed the pipe from his mouth, taking care not to break the continuity of the thick, ever-lengthening skein of almost-solid mucus that trailed from the pipe-stem to his toothless maw.

He spoke slowly.

'How's she cuttin', lads?' said he.

It was one of those meaningless enquiries to which English tourists seldom know how to respond.

I smoothly lapsed into patois and executed the correct response as expected.

'Cuttin' grand don't you know boy!' sez I.

'So!' he countered, for no obvious reason.

I warmed to the dialect. 'Are there not a few lumps of lads knockin' about here somewhere?' I enquired.

He seemed not to hear. A look of urgency tinged with alarm crossed his face. Ill-advisedly placing the smouldering pipe on his lap, he quickly lifted his full pint of stout and tilted it swiftly and expertly. Most of it gurgled noisily down his throat. The rest ran down his chin and disappeared behind his surprisingly filthy vest. Glass still lodged in right hand, he placed his other hand on his left knee and forced himself forward at what constituted a dangerous angle. The lit pipe teetered precariously on his lap. He seemed on the point of tipping over. I reached out instinctively to check his imminent tumble but, just before I reached him, he farted noisily and sprung back to his original position.

He retrieved the pipe from deep within his smouldering nether regions and assumed his original position.

'Better out than in,' he remarked.

This is what this country needs, I thought—men who are slow to talk but quick to fart.

'The lads you're lookin' for are in the snug,' he said. 'They're not all friendly, are they?'

'No,' I said. 'They're not.'

The snug was located at the far end of the bar. As we made our way towards it, the bald proprietor of the establishment emerged from a dark recess behind the counter.

We sensed he was the proprietor by his aura of natural cunning, ruddy complexion, ferret-like face, knowing eyes and bald pumpkin head.

He eyed us suspiciously and bared his fangs in what, in his wary world, may have passed for a smile.

'All right, lads?' he said.

'The very finest,' I replied. 'We'll have half-a-dozen Cokes, please. In the snug, if you will.

'Rightyar,' he slowly replied, surreptitiously eyeballing the brown bags we carried.

I edged open the wooden half-door of the snug and defined the outline of four bodies in the murk.

Harpo, Lashback, Ray and Pat sat enveloped in swirls of cigarette smoke, hunched over three pints of stout and a disproportionately large number of balls of malt.

'Unsociable shower of bastards!' I cried, by way of greeting. 'What the fuck are you doing holed up in here like dogs in quarantine! You should be outside in full view talking to the natives. Be seen to be nice. Mingle. Always mingle.'

'Mingle with who? The talking corpse at the bar?' Harpo snorted.

'The corpse to which you refer has noticed that you people aren't very friendly,' I said. 'We need to be careful. That's how orchestras like

ours get a bad name. It's bad for business. Smile and be nice to the punters, whomsoever they may be.'

'Fuck them,' Harpo said, in fluent East Belfast.

'Precisely,' I replied.

'Time to scarper,' said Harpo, hoisting his frame upright in a business-like manner.

He seemed overly anxious to leave. It was 5.30 in the afternoon. In three-and-a-half hours' time we were due to take the stage in some windblown, isolated ballroom somewhere in darkest Donegal. Time was tight. It was a hundred-and-fifty miles to wherever it was we were headed.

'If we don't leave now we'll miss whatever grub is going.'

I reached under the table and noisily shook a brown paper bag. 'Relax, Your Harpness,' I announced. 'Food will not figure highly on our agenda tonight!'

Harpo sighed and sank back heavily into his seat. He knew we weren't going anywhere for a while.

This exchange attracted the attention of Lashback and Ray who until this moment had paid little or no heed to what was going on around them.

Lashback swivelled a hooded eye in my direction.

'Whatsya got there, head?' he drawled.

Lashback was our drummer and, consequently, I had to be careful not to expose him to too much stimulation. He was docile at the moment but this could quickly change. He had the classic drummer's face, long and lachrymose, topped by a shock of straight, jet-black shoulder-length hair. Clad in scruffy loon pants, ersatz Indian moccasins and a none-too-fragrant T-shirt, he was rangy, lithe and pre-dictably unpredictable—a man prone to sudden outbreaks of frenetic activity. Particularly fond of dropping acid (LSD to you) he claimed to suffer frequent flashbacks which, as every schoolboy knows, are due to the drug momentarily reasserting itself after the user's body has apparently recovered from the last intake. He had once tried to explain this anomaly to Harpo who, of course, misheard a section of the infor-mation offered and subsequently referred to our chemically enhanced percussionist as 'Lashback.'

Harpo eyed the bag lazily.

I was distracted by a loud knock on the door of the snug. A red, pock-marked bald head appeared.

'Six Cokes was it?'

'How kind of you, innkeeper. Edward, compensate the gentleman for his trouble,' I boomed. I liked to talk this way when confronted by shifty little publicans. It confused them.

Eddie reluctantly fumbled within the depths of his fur-trimmed pockets and produced some coins of the realm.

Accepting the remuneration, the proprietor leaned against the door and squinted at us.

'Ye're a band. Aren't ye?'

'Give that man a kewpie doll!' I exclaimed. 'Got it in one, sir. And may I say how impressed we are by the high standards pertaining in your establishment. The world will beat a path to your door when word leaks out of your existence.'

'Do ye have an engagement tonight?'

'We do indeed, sir. In the uniquely beautiful though sadly neglected, nay, spurned, county of Donegal. A place of great beauty, solitude and, if I may say so, the birthplace of my own mother and her siblings.'

The pumpkin head stared at me blankly.

'Have ye any schnapps?' it asked.

'That would be your area,' I replied. 'You're the man who sells the drink.'

He seemed puzzled.

'Photographs of the band I'm after,' he added, hopefully.

I realised he was referring to the postcard-sized publicity photographs that showbands usually dole out to punters after gigs.

'I'm afraid we're fresh out of snaps. Sorry.' I replied.

'For a minute there, I thought we were back in fucking Germany,' roared Lashback with an ugly laugh.

Baldy's face tightened. He spoke.

'Donegal, eh? That's quite a jaunt from here. Cuttin' it a bit fine, aren't yez?'

'A man after me own heart.' Harpo interjected. 'It's hard to shift these fuckers sometimes.'

Baldy suddenly became a little edgy. 'Yez won't be any trouble lads, will yez?'

He'd finally sensed that we weren't the same as normal people.

'Perish the thought, landlord.' I replied. 'You shall neither hear nor see us. We value the privacy of your well-appointed snug.'

'Well,' he said testily,' you know where I am if you need anything else.'

'Thank you kindly,' ventured I. 'We already have altogether more than we require.'

The door of the snug closed.

Ray came to life.

'Why are you winding him up?'

'Winding who up?'

'The fucking Johnny of the pub. You shouldn't talk to people that way.'

'What way?'

'Talking that shite talk. You can see it's making him nervous. He thinks you're taking the piss.'

'I'm only winding him up.'

'Isn't that what I just said?'

'We are sensitive today, little Orange chap, aren't we?'

Ray was sensitive most days. Like Billy, Harpo and me, he was from the North, but he wasn't like me at all. Not that I was exemplary in any way. God knows I was just as unstable and warped as he was. No, my problems lay in different areas. Ray was haunted by demons, the nature of which I could only but speculate. He had long ago hit rock bottom and broken clean through to a yet lower level about which I knew nothing.

He was of average height with pipe-cleaner legs that had atrophied through lack of even the most rudimentary form of exercise. He was the only person I had ever encountered whose legs knocked audibly together when, confronted by an emergency, they were forced to scuttle across short distances. He also abhorred any form of daylight.

On the other hand, he played saxophone with frightening venom and could do something with the instrument that I had hitherto thought impossible. Whilst playing a solo, he could both swear and blow simultaneously. Each batch of three or four notes violently squeezed from the horn were accompanied by an audible 'fuck.'

After completing their journey through the microphone, these clearly enunciated 'fucks' could often be clearly heard all over the dance hall. The more sober patrons had occasionally noticed this and sometimes brought it to the attention of members of the band who, of course, shrugged off the complaints and blamed the acoustics of the house. But this was just a behavioural tic.

Ray's main problem was that he was torn apart by Ulster Presbyterian Guilt. This is a peculiarly Northern-Irish trait. Billy suffered the occasional twinge, but the others were unfamiliar with the concept. I, having studied it at close hand during my formative years, understood. The more Ray drank, fornicated and generally behaved badly, the more he despised himself. It was a dangerous spiral of despair but not uncommon amongst his people. George Best was a contemporary of Ray's, once a neighbour too, back in Belfast. George would have understood.

And Ray had quite a pedigree. He also played keyboards and flute, and had once been a member of Them, the first rock group (or 'beat group' as they were called then) from Belfast to crack the British charts. They'd had a few big ones, 'Baby, Please Don't Go', 'Gloria,' 'Here Comes the Night,' featuring, of course, Van Morrison on vocals. That original group had crashed and burned but Ray was part of the reconstituted Them, which broke up in mid-1966. That was the last Them. But at least he'd been there and had enjoyed a sniff of the big time.

Ray had been a member of the resident band in the Plaza Ballroom in Belfast, and, like many a good man before him, was signing on the dole as well. 'Doing the Double' has always been part of the Northern musician's economic life—factored into all equations. The generosity of Her Majesty the Queen has always been greatly acknowledged and appreciated in Northern musical households.

According to Ray, Van was down and out at the time. However, he was thrown somewhat of a life-line when his recording of a song called 'Richard Cory', appeared in the charts on the West Coast of America. Asked to put a band together in order to undertake a coffers-replenishing tour of the Western seaboard, Van then did what people do when they need musicians in a hurry.

He stood outside the dole in Belfast and waited to see who emerged.

What is a saxophone player to do when, after signing on for a few quid a day, he leaves a grey dole and is making his way to the equally grey and grimy Plaza Ballroom in Chichester Street, where he will play music for five hours to strumpets and drunken sailors, and a short, stocky man suddenly steps from the shadows and asks him if he wants to go to California? Like any red-blooded man would, Ray said 'yes.'

With hardly time to draw breath, Ray found himself on a plane bound for San Francisco. He was about to be introduced to the philosophy of Flower Power by those who invented it.

This is how he put it to me: 'We didn't rehearse or anything, just talked about how we would get through a few numbers, blues and that, and the Richard Cory thing which was wee buns anyway. Next thing I knew, we were in San Francisco surrounded by people who were smiling all the time. I thought they were nuts. Anyway, we got hardly any sleep before we were taken to the first gig. I found out later that it was the Fillmore West. I was standing at the side of the stage, jet-lagged, barely able to hold my saxophone up, when we were announced and ushered on the stage. First thing I seen was Van jumping up on the speakers about ten feet high and dancing like a madman. He would've killed himself if he'd fallen off. There was a huge drop on the other side. Then a big screen dropped down behind us about forty feet tall and they showed a film featuring a naked woman with her legs open and u.s. Army tanks coming out of her box. I said to myself: 'What the fuck is this?'

Welcome to California.

Ray embraced the life for a while, hanging out with the likes of Frank Zappa's Mothers of Invention, who apparently liked the way he talked.

Van, however, disappeared and went to New York.

Them went home and Van recorded *Astral Weeks*.

Maybe he didn't need the band after all.

Over the course of a few years Ray eventually drifted back to Belfast. He did not relish the company of the likes of us. He should have stayed in California. Forced by the escalating Troubles in Belfast to subsist in Dublin earning a living tootling his horn, he regarded himself as a superior being in all ways and was firmly convinced that all Dubliners and people from the south of Ireland in general were inferior beings.

There were many like him Up There. After all, in essence, that was why people like me were Down Here. In weaker moments I felt sorry for him. The band, as a more-or-less functioning entity, tried to understand this and learned to live with his idiosyncrasies. We could accommodate diversity and he wasn't a bad saxophone player, amplified fucks or no.

A gloomy and dispiriting presence, though.

His companion on the front line was Pat, though Billy sometimes played a bit of saxophone too if inspiration struck him at a time when he had consumed just the right amount of drink. But for the most part, our brass section consisted of Ray on fucking saxophone and Pat on trombone.

Having a soft spot for trombone players, I liked Pat. He didn't belong in a band like ours. He was too nice a person. He knew in his heart that he was in over his head but had little choice other than to stay with the outfit until something civilised materialised.

Pat always looked, well, very clean. He had missed his vocation in life. God had meant him to be an accountant. He was quietly spoken and dressed in a neatly conservative manner. His hair was long but tidy. He visibly worried about his future and seemed scared of us. Women fancied him but he didn't seem to see them. We noticed this and tut-tutted at the waste.

Even now whilst the others, including myself, were feverishly crushing the plastic casing of the sinus aids in order to release the contents for immediate immersion into far-from-clean glassware, containing the traditional mixture of Coke and now whiskey (because the day was progressing apace), pausing only a minute or two before squeezing the last remaining trace of benzedrine into the foul brew, Pat sat quietly on a stool nursing a bottle of stout—a man apart. Not for him the sudden rush of energy shooting up the spinal column, nor for him the ceaseless pacing of the floor whilst jabbering bollocks about Charlie Parker, nor need he endure the teeth-grinding boredom that seemed to rapidly descend upon the rest of us when there was a lull and things didn't appear to be happening as quickly as they should. No, he didn't need any of that. He was content with his own values, happy to smile sadly and shake his head as he watched us children play. In fairness to him, he did not disapprove, nor did he beseech us to change our ways.

But, taking the long view, he was lucky to be with us, or, indeed, with anyone. He had once played in a version of the Miami Showband but the Dickie Dream hadn't worked out. Methinks in retrospect he'd made the right career move after all. If he'd stayed with the Miami, the odds on him being still around to observe our worrying behaviour would have been extremely thin. The odds were just about even that he would've ended up in a ditch with a bullet in his back.

As a consequence of being in the wrong job and with the wrong people, he spoke hesitantly and seemed unsure of what was happening at any given time. The rest of us, on the other hand, didn't give much of a fuck about what was happening at any particular time and were therefore less likely to fret.

The Benzedrine was starting to take hold. Lashback, as drummers do, tended to babble most. He held his pint of Guinness aloft and peered at it.

'Where are we?' he said.

'What do you mean?' answered Harpo, running an edgy hand through his flaxen thatch.

Lashback still stared wildly at his raised stout. 'Where the fuck are we, I said,' he repeated. 'How many other ways can I say it?'

'You mean now?'

'Yes, I mean now, today.'

'Somewhere between Drogheda and Dundalk. Why?'

'The pint shouldn't be cloudy here. We're not in the North yet.'

'Oh.'

Eddie had no idea what that meant. Nor did he seek an explanation. Lashback's general conversation often did not make conventional sense. He slapped the pint heavily onto the table, spilling a little. It was clear that he was edgy. We were used to that. He was congenitally temperamental.

'Guinness is good for you, isn't that what they say?' he yelped.

'That's how they talk it up,' yawned Harpo.

'Exactly.'

'So.'

'Advertisers are a shower of bastards. Why can't they tell us the truth for a change.'

Lashback was excited, lapsing into his theatrical voice—deep and booming. It was in his blood. His real name was Pat Nash, a show business brat, son of venerable actor Cecil Nash, one-time doyen of the Dublin theatre and active participant in high-profile movies such as *Where's Jack?*, *Rocket to the Moon* and, famously, to me anyway, *Of*

Human Bondage, in which he played the father of the boy with the club foot. Because of that, I often fantasised about Lashback having a club foot and struggling to operate the bass-drum pedal. Well, it passed the time.

He was standing now, club footless, gesticulating wildly.

'Why can't they use an advertising slogan that we can identify with, something that's informative, something that tells us something fundamentally true about the national product. Something that some of us may not be aware of? Something educational?'

'Like what?'

'How about this? "GUINNESS MAKES YOUR SHITE TURN BLACK!" Let's see that on the billboards!' He cackled and sat down heavily. He suddenly looked as if he might fall asleep. I knew better. Lashback's outward signs did not signal the same things as did outward signs displayed by others. He would have to be watched closely.

This was shaping up to be a long day.

I glanced towards Eddie and could see that he was uncomfortable. Probably nothing to do with Lashback, whom he liked. I always knew when Eddie was upset. He had a tell-tale habit of tilting his head at angle of approximately seventy-five degrees to the horizontal when vexed.

I shuffled over and sat beside him on the narrow bench. Noting that he was surrounded by the remains of half-a-dozen inhalers, I knew I'd have to be careful with him too.

'You OK?' I enquired.

Wha?'

'Lashback's a mad bastard, isn't he?' I chuckled reassuringly.

Eddie didn't seem to hear.

'She won't get into trouble, will she?' he mumbled.

'Who?'

'The charver working in the place we got the nose jobs.'

Bless his heart. I'd forgotten. Eddie had a conscience. He worried about civilians.

I lifted the glass in front of him. A finger of whiskey remained.

'Get that down you,' I commanded. 'And don't you trouble your bollocks about any of that.'

But it was too late. He wanted to talk.

Eddie and I had history. We had both played together in a band called The Chessmen before we'd joined this outfit. The Chessmen were a cheerier bunch, less fatalistic, more human.

'It was better before,' murmured Eddie. The inhalers and whiskey were getting to him.

'No,' I said. 'Not necessarily better. Different.'

'D'you remember Hammerman?'

Ah, the old nostalgia spectacles.

'Hammerman' was the nickname of one of the guys in The Chessmen. The term 'hammerman' *per se*, is applied, exclusively within the showband brotherhood, to those amongst us who are blessed with a particular talent for finding and fucking large numbers of women—serial fornicators. This talent is a gift. It can't be acquired. You either have it or you don't.

Eddie admired him greatly. Hammerman was the man Eddie wanted to be but a natural reticence held him back. He was also too nice a person. No hammerman worth the name can afford to be understanding, sentimental or caring. Eddie was all three. Eddie couldn't be Hammerman because Eddie cared about women as human beings. No potential hammerman can function under such a handicap.

Eddie's face seemed to cloud over with bliss.

'Remember he used to have them sorted before the dances even started?'

'How could I forget?'

'I often wondered how he did that.'

'He kept his eyes open, that's how. You could've done the same. If you'd wanted to…'

'I never had the nerve.'

It was true. Hammerman used to have three or four women lined up before he went on stage.

And then there was that thing he used to do in marquees.

'Remember that thing he used to do in marquees?' said Eddie, wistfully.

'I always thought that was a step too far,' I tut-tutted.

And it was. Hammerman never failed. But he really shone when the Big Top loomed.

Before the commencement of each marquee dance, whilst we were floundering about in the mud trying to get into our band suits, Hammerman would pace the quagmire anxiously until his first victim showed up.

Hammerman had a canvas fetish, the only such fetish I have ever heard of or encountered. It's a rare condition. I blame childhood visits to the circus and premature exposure to dark-eyed Italian girls wearing damaged fishnet tights shinning up a rope with another lump of hemp wrapped round their boxes, climbing sensuously towards the high trapeze, all the while displaying perfectly proportioned pear-shaped Mediterranean arses to the mooning faces of a gripped immature audience below who'd seen enough of clowns.

Sights like that can affect a boy during his formative years.

For the simple-minded, let me reiterate that most marquee tents are constructed of large swathes of canvas lashed together by stout ropes. Nevertheless, between each tied section of canvas there is usually an opening from top to bottom, two or three inches wide, the purpose of which, in my experience, is to facilitate the entry of biting Arctic winds. Hammerman discovered that there were other uses to which a split in a tent could be put.

Eventually, a female voice from the outside would be heard gently cooing through one of these openings.

'Are you there, Rick?' was the usual opening gambit.

Rick wasn't Hammerman's real name, of course. It was one of his pseudonyms. He was also fond of Sidney. I had never warmed to Sidney, too spiv-like.

Hammerman would then spring lithely towards the gap in the canvas.

We, who knew what was about to unfold, would listen carefully to his lecherous mumblings, directed outwards…

In the fullness of time, his hand would eventually slither though the gap in the awning and a one-sided fumbling would begin.

Then, rudimentary foreplay completed, he would rasp something like (and I paraphrase), 'Turn round and put your arse up against the opening.'

Upon the completion of this manoeuvre, Hammerman would then swiftly drop his strides and, through the gap, loudly fornicate with whatever slouched outside the tent.

Throughout this blessed coupling, Hammerman would stare at us wild-eyed though somehow blindly, but, nevertheless, still find time to offer a sporadic thumbs-up. The sight of this rampant male in full rut stays with me to this day. It renders the word 'aesthetics' meaningless.

This is what mankind is really like. And this is why we're here. To reproduce by any means possible. All the rest is padding.

When he had completed this public act of gross indecency, he would swiftly disengage, pull up his trousers, and casually walk away, ignoring the tiny, pleading, whimpering sounds floating in from the other side of the burlap.

No post-coital reassurances there.

'How did he talk them into humiliating themselves like that,' wondered Eddie.' What did they see in him?'

'Raw animal magnetism,' I said. 'It's Nature, red in tooth and claw.'

'And that's it?'

'What else is there? I'd settle for it. It's better than fuck-all.'

Eddie cracked open another phial of nose medicine and gnawed hungrily at the impregnated cotton wad.

'Jesus, Eddie!' I yelped. 'Take it easy. You'll poison yourself.'

He didn't seem to hear.

'And remember when we had that puncture near Monaghan?' he said, seemingly oblivious to the chemical foulness in his mouth.

'Not sure.'

'Of course, you do. Just outside of town and we all sat on the ditch watching the grease monkey from the garage trying get the wheel off? Sunny day. Remember?'

'It's coming back to me.'

'And the two girls out for an innocent stroll?'

'Uh-huh.'

'We were only there ten minutes. And Hammerman had never met them before in his life?'

'And he went behind the hedge and fucked the two of them?'

'You do remember!'

'Yeah. That was quick. Even for him,' I wistfully remarked.

'I wish I could do that. I miss him.'

He dropped his head a little. I could see that the chemicals coursing through his system were working against him.

Time to go.

———

When we could delay no longer, we vacated the premises and bade a strained farewell to a proprietor glad to see the back of us. I suspect he disliked us not because we'd behaved badly, which we hadn't, but because we'd conducted ourselves in a manner that he'd found vaguely unacceptable but wasn't sure why.

When we struggled out onto the street, a number of urchins had gathered around the van. This is always a problem in small towns and villages. It doesn't do to tell them to fuck off as elders, siblings, guardians or perhaps parents are watching through twitching curtains.

'Are yese famous?' inquired a snot-streaked, semi-ragged lad, clutching at Ray's coat as he climbed in to the van.

'Fuck aff, sonny,' snarled Ray in his best Belfast shipyard accent.

10

In between being shown bits and pieces on guitar by Sean Reilly and finally giving up the idea of someday owning the white plastic alto saxophone nestling in Deery's shop window, I momentarily dallied with the notion of becoming a singer. Nowadays, I recoil in horror at the thought, but I suppose this was a stage I had to go through, a *rite de passage.*

I'd made the mistake of going to see Billy Fury in Saint Columb's Hall in Derry. To my surprise, there was something about this tubercular ex-Liverpool tugboat hand that appealed to me. For a start, he looked as if he didn't expect to live very long. For some reason, this idea seemed persuasive at the time. There were two things in his favour: (a) he could sneer like Elvis, and (b) he starred in a film called *I've Gotta Horse*, which was probably the worst British pop movie ever made (and, yes, I have seen the Dave Clark Five in *Catch Us if you Can*).

His act seemed to consist of spending an inordinate amount of time attempting to dry-hump the microphone stand. I had never seen this before. I was further impressed by the fact that the girls in front of the stage seemed eager to participate. Anything that reduced these normally hard-to-crack scrubbers to a randy, willing, slavering state like this must have something going for it, I thought. It was also illuminating to note that Billy Fury couldn't sing at all.

I had also, courtesy of my brother Johnny, met Adam Faith. He wasn't as sickly looking as Fury, merely deathly pale. I was in a privileged position. Adam Faith, then at the apex of his popularity, was due to appear at the Corinthian Ballroom in Derry that night. He was also scheduled to rehearse with his band in the hall that afternoon and, Johnny, as a member of the regular local support band booked to play the lion's share of the dance that night, had every right to be there. He decided to take me with him. It was the first time I had been inside a place of entertainment in the afternoon. There is nothing more dispiriting.

I expected a little excitement—a trace of stardust. After all, to be in the presence of Adam Faith and his band ('Poor Me', 'What Do You Want If You Don't Want Money')!

And there was the star himself, a tiny, insignificant scruffy figure, overcoat too big, draped loosely over hunched, scrawny shoulders, desultorily sipping a cup of tea. His band lounged about the stage tootling and pecking at their instruments in a half-hearted manner. No stardust there. From the street outside could be heard the clang of dustbins as the refuse-disposal men went about their business. The fake romance and perceived glamour of a ballroom or nightclub swiftly dissipate in harsh daylight when the everyday sounds of the workaday world are allowed to filter through.

Adam Faith was bored and tired. Even I could see that. Johnny suggested we approach him and perhaps exchange a word or two. Something within me knew better.

I loitered whilst Adam Faith and his band did everything in their power to postpone the moment when they had to rehearse. Yes, being Adam Faith was just a job like any other. Billy Fury probably didn't much enjoy being Billy Fury either. He lasted longer than I thought he would. His heart didn't kill him until he was forty-two. Adam Faith was healthier and smarter than Billy Fury. His heart didn't kill him until he was sixty-two.

After further study of local singers in bands, I concluded that most of them were adult versions of the loud, needy children whom nobody liked at school.

Nor was their status within bands as high as one would expect.

My brother Johnny confirmed my suspicions. 'Guess what?' he said, one afternoon, carefully coaxing his long greasy hair into an architecturally impossible pompadour at the front and concomitant duck's arse at the rear of the skull. 'Jumpin' Johnny's out of the picture.'

This could mean either that Jumpin' Johnny Lee, the singer in one of my brother's outfits, had left the band or had been sacked.

'Sacked?' I muttered in a worldly way.

'Naw.' Johnny was gnawing on some gum, Beechnut, as I recall. 'Can't take it. Nerves got the better of him.'

'Nerves' was a euphemism employed to cover a variety of ailments or failings. It was used to refer to conditions as diverse as stage-fright, common illness, schizophrenia, alcoholism, dependence on any number of drugs, marital breakdown, depression, bankruptcy, cancer or being evicted from one's home.

Even I knew that when a person was said to be suffering from 'nerves', no further enquiry was required or welcome.

I used to like watching Jumpin' Johnny and did so whenever I could. He used to front a band called Johnny and the Jokers. Their handouts (schnapps) were in the form of a hand of playing cards, a band member's head replacing the denomination of each of the cards. Those fucking ideas again. Dogs, playing cards, dwarves, masks, grass skirts...

But what a mover. He was nearly handsome but not quite. He looked like an Italian who'd been punched in the face. He also looked permanently terrified. I discovered that women seemed to like that, often mistaking a genuine terror of all things earthly as a sign of sensitivity and vulnerability—the Montgomery Clift Syndrome.

Jumpin' was a man who strove mightily to justify his name. I particularly liked the way he chose to make his entrance on to the stage. He would hover stage right, tense and coiled like a cobra. Cue an ill-executed, ragged drum roll from a giggling drummer and a bandleader's arm carelessly flung in Jumpin' Johnny's direction with the fabled announcement: 'And nigh ladies and gennelmin, put your hands til gether for the singing sensation of the age. HEY! IT'S JUMPIN' JOHNNY LEE AND (short pause for effect) BOY (another pause) CAN HE JUMP!'

As if shot from a cannon, Jumpin' would launch himself into the air by means of a truly Olympian bound that would carry him centre stage where he would touchdown to the mighty crash of a Zildjian cymbal— a quick shimmy, a toss of the Roman curls, then straight into 'High School Confidential' by Jerry Lee Lewis.

'Joining another outfit, is he?' I enquired.

'No. It's nerves,' Johnny said. 'They're shot.'

'Oh...'

'No big deal.'

'He'll be hard to replace. He's popular,' speculated I.

Johnny laughed scornfully and scooped another handful of Brylcreem from the jumbo jar. 'Dime a dozen. We'll just open another can of singers, and put a suit on the one at the top. They're all the same.'

I sensed little respect there.

Most lead singers and drummers in bands were regarded as non-musicians by the so-called musicians in the band. Some even regarded them as sub-human. And there is some truth in this.

Drummers are often loud and boorish, singers egotistical and narcissistic.

Lead singers never die, they just withdraw into a fantasy world. I met one recently whilst he was struggling up a steep street in Derry. He was not as young as he used to be, was feeling the passage of time and had the kind of rheumy eye that bode ill for his short-term future.

'All the good singers are dying,' he said suddenly.

'I hadn't noticed,' I replied.

'Of course, you have. They're all gone. Bing Crosby, Nat King Cole, Perry Como, Frank Sinatra, all gone.'

'I suppose you're right.'

'And do you know what?' he said, looking sadly at the raised palm of his hand.

'What?'

'I don't feel too well myself.'

I thought maybe I'd be better off playing an instrument after all. That's when I bought a guitar. It was an old Framus acoustic with too much space between the strings and fingerboard. Guitars were cheap, even the dogs in the street were playing them, so mastering the basics didn't seem too daunting a task.

After a month or so the fingertips on my left hand were so mangled and bloody I felt I was getting somewhere. I ran into one or two guys I'd been to school with. They had formed what they'd described as a skiffle group and invited me to come strum with them. They gathered on a weekly basis, at one of their homes. I sensed a problem right away. I would have to travel to the other side of Derry carrying a guitar. I had no case or suitable guitar cover with which to even partially camouflage the offending guitar. I knew it was a jungle out there, the streets were infested by people of my own age who regarded someone lugging a guitar as, at best, a cissy or, at worst, a practising homosexual. Remember this was the late fifties, not the most enlightened or tolerant of times. Television sets in the home were uncommon and life was lived on the street.

———

Radio didn't keep young people in at nights. Every street corner or junction was crawling with sullen, bored youths who spat on the pavement every ten seconds whilst their eyes darted about in search of some form of diversion. A nerd bearing a guitar was akin to a limping, asthmatic wildebeest calf struggling alone across the Serengeti. But there were worse things to carry than a guitar. Who knew what unspeakable abominations lay in store for the child spotted toting a violin? But even the treatment doled out to captured violinists was mild compared to the insults, humiliation and physical damage endured by any boy wearing a skirt and unfortunate enough to be intercepted on his way home from Irish dancing classes.

Some acts of nature, such as how long it really takes a pride of lions to kill a wildebeest, are better not considered.

On foot, of course, and concealing the guitar as best I could by wrapping it in one of my father's old overcoats that hung in perpetuity behind our kitchen door, I dared travel only after dark, even then adhering to a carefully pre-plotted route that avoided all major T-junctions and corners where rabble traditionally gathered. Scuttling along in the merciful shadows of the city's medieval walls and scurrying down littered alleyways like a plague rat, I was seldom spotted.

But I wasn't always lucky. With pounding heart, I would sometimes hear the distant war-cry of: 'Look! It's fuckin' Elvis!' Then a sudden rush of feet and the hunt was on. Like the noble stag, I sometimes got away, sometimes not. No man who wants to cover ground swiftly is advised to run burdened by a full-bodied guitar wrapped in his father's overcoat. Often as not I was bushwhacked or dry-gulched, surrounded by leering faces emitting foul breath, and forced to endure being pushed about by nicotine-stained hands.

'Sing us a song, cunt,' a music lover would inevitably suggest.

It was possible to withdraw only by unfurling the guitar, jettisoning the overcoat and whirling the instrument above my head like Excalibur whilst backing towards the next darkened alleyway on my route, an alleyway that would inevitably lead me to another swathe of enemy territory, teeming with more scumbags.

This was the nature of my first contact with large groups of people whilst holding a guitar, and whereas I hesitate to describe my torturers as an 'audience', I found it difficult in the future to think of the paying public as anything less than potentially hostile. These street encounters during which my guitar had merit only as a weapon surely sowed the seeds of the deep unease I continue to feel today when confronted by a fresh audience.

Sometimes it's not easy to come to terms with that difficult early stuff…

——

The skies darkened early as the coach rattled along towards Dundalk. We had previously decided to take the long route to Donegal, via Belfast and Derry. Apparently, Billy had something to pick up in Belfast. Well, he was head honcho and called the shots.

Harpo paid no attention to the potholes that peppered the roads and ploughed on regardless at a reckless rate of knots. 'It's a wonder you wouldn't do something about the state of the fuckin' roads down here. Third world or fuckin' what!' Harpo yelled back over his shoulder to nobody in particular.

'Jayus, Harpo!' shrieked Eddie, from his billet just behind the driver's seat. 'Just because the roads aren't great doesn't mean you have to drive like we're on the fucking autobahn. Take her easy, for fuck's sake. I'm touching cloth here.'

'Don't be such a baby,' said Harpo, jerking suddenly to the right in the act of recklessly overtaking a startled tractor driver whose meandering trailer contained what looked like a ton of condemned veal.

Eddie didn't travel well. He'd nearly been killed in one of these things before. I had been present too and hadn't been killed either. It happened when we were both with The Chessmen, on our way home from a gig in the Arcadia Ballroom in Cork. Most of the band were asleep by the time we reached Portlaoise, roughly half-way between Dublin and Cork. It was a long-bodied, well-fitted-out coach, much like the one we were travelling in today. There were four rows of seats, not including the driver's perch. I was reading in the back seat with my miner's helmet firmly in place when I noticed the driver slump forward, overcome by fatigue.

I had two options. One was to race up the aisle, take the wheel manfully, keeping the machine between the hedges until such time as the driver snapped out of his ill-timed nap and was sufficiently *compos mentis* to take control, or, two, to burrow down in my seat, scream, cower like a dog and wait. I, of course, chose the latter option. What if the coach had hit something before I'd reached the driver? Possibly curtains, I calculated.

There is a life-defining elongated nanosecond that passes between the realisation that a crash is inevitable and actual impact. At moments like these, a person begins to understand the Theory of Relativity.

Then the hideous screams as bodies are thrown arse-over-tit, the terrifying tearing of base metals, the potentially lethal rapid repositioning of bass drums, guitar cases, microphone stands and other life-threatening bric-a-brac hurtling forward from the back, followed finally by the post-shunt eerie silence that eventually gives way to the low moans of survivors.

We had thundered through a roadside hedge, tumbled four feet into a field below and slid sideways for about fifty yards before toppling and eventually slowing to a halt. Luckily, nothing solid (tree, anyone?) had detained us before the coach came to rest. Nevertheless, everybody was hurt except me. My decision to cling to the potential wreckage had been justified. Eddie was particularly traumatised and had his arm in a splint for weeks, not something that most guitar players look forward to.

But Harpo hadn't crashed yet.

I gazed out of the window and watched the world whiz by as I furiously drummed on my kneecaps with urgent fingers. The Benzedrine was doing its work. The legacy of the foul stuff also explained the inflamed eyes through which I observed wisps of smoke gently curl from old-fashioned chimney pots perched atop whitewashed picture-book cottages. Patchwork fields populated by a variety of mangy animals stretched before us as far as the eye could see. Agricultural people were out there, leading ordinary agricultural lives. We didn't fit in, didn't blend with the landscape—we were interlopers.

Another small village suddenly appeared and Harpo was forced to remove his boot from the accelerator in order to avoid mowing down hapless civilians who didn't deserve to die.

At this point another voice was heard—a small, eerie unworldly sound. 'WILLIAM HENNESSEY & SON, RELIGIOUS OBJECTS AND FANCY GOODS.'

It was the sound of Ray's Ritual Rollcall. We hadn't heard it for a while.

'JAMES A. PORTER, FLESHER,' Ray intoned, this time in a stronger, more sepulchral voice. He was limbering up.

Ray was reading aloud, beginning in a low-pitched monotone and gradually working up to a bellow, the signs above the village shops as we drove by.

We were half-way through the village.

Louder now: 'PETER O'ROURKE, WINES AND SPIRITS.'

Ray would soon be on his feet for the last reading.

None of us were quite sure why he did this. When asked, he would merely smile. I suppose it was just a psychological tic. On long journeys, and also on short ones come to think of it, this was his only contribution to the admittedly sparse conversation engaged in by members of the band. We didn't talk to each other much when travelling. Maybe other bands did. We had no way of knowing.

As the hamlet petered out Ray was on his feet screaming, 'PATRICK FLAHERTY, GENTLEMEN'S OUTFITTERS!'

He then resumed his seated position, stroked his beard thoughtfully and stared glumly at the countryside as it continued to flash by.

Ray's Ritual Rollcall was unnerving at first but we'd had to get used to it. However, it could become a trial whilst driving through largish conurbations where there were many shops and businesses displaying what Americans in old movies referred to as 'shingles'.

It didn't bother me. It annoyed Eddie though, sitting beside me. He was wound a little tighter than the rest.

'Why doesn't he shut the fuck up?' Eddie muttered through clenched teeth.

'Tolerance, Eddie,' I replied. 'Tolerance.'

11

E
ddie and I had been through much together. We'd been to hell
and back with The Chessmen. The Chessmen were never a showband either in the accepted sense of the word. They'd started out
in the mid-to-early sixties playing small dives, basements and tennis
clubs in Dublin. They were what used to be innocently known as a 'beat
group'.

Amongst their ranks, however, was a fairly talented and somewhat
charismatic singer-songwriter/organist called Alan Dee. Popular in a
local way, the group somehow found their way into a studio where they
recorded what they preferred to think of as worthy, original songs.
During that session they also laid down a spoof track called 'Michael
Murphy's Boy', a simple piece of paddywhackery about a naïve young
Irishman off to England to make his fortune. They released a worthy
single and, off-handedly perhaps, put 'Michael Murphy's Boy' on the
flip-side.

Much to the puzzlement and, I imagine, dismay of the band,
'Michael Murphy's Boy', entered the Irish charts, a genuine hit. It is a
measure of how little value the band placed on things Irish at the time
that they were so surprised by the song's popularity. Listening to it with
today's ears, it sounds, clever, catchy and trendily ironic.

A bona-fide smash with a locally penned original song was a rarity
indeed and the band were encouraged to augment and join the lucrative showband circuit.

This they did, adding a brass section, reluctantly kitting themselves
out with shiny suits. The show-band version of The Chessmen was, of
course, bound to fail. After an initial period of mild success followed by
a couple of plodding years, half the band, including Dee, jumped ship.

This was where I came in. I replaced Robert Ballagh, the now revered
and critically unassailable artist. He'd had more than enough and
allegedly gave his bass to a young man called Phil Lynott, who had
expressed an interest in taking up the instrument. By the time I joined,
the band was disillusioned and demoralised. That suited me fine

because I had never been in a band that had felt any differently. I suppose I was just lucky.

As a general rule of thumb, if a man found himself in a showband that was disillusioned and demoralised, he could be reasonably confident that he was amongst sensitive and, often, intelligent people. It was the nature of the business.

Although aware that there were many happy and contented bands out there, I had no experience of playing in one. Travelling the less popular road tends to build character.

The Chessmen found it difficult to find a new singer. Wiser counsel decreed that the search be extended to England, where there was a better chance of snaring a 'name.' The year was 1966, by which time the success of The Beatles and those who followed had almost wiped out the solo or 'ballad' singer, especially the kind of home-grown warbler predominant in the late fifties and early sixties. Men of dubious calibre like Eden Kane, Jimmy Justice, Vince Eager and Ricky Valance had been rendered obsolete practically overnight.

Only rare exceptions among those with engineered names (Georgie Fame, Adam Faith) had enough talent to adjust and ride with the times. Rumour had it that even Cliff himself felt the pinch.

However, in backward Mother Ireland, these names still retained a little magic and a more-than-welcome whiff of stardust. A British ex-star would be of novelty value for a short time and could perhaps extend the shelf-life of a band like The Chessmen whose members never gave much of a fuck to begin with.

So, through a third party, our management applied themselves to the task of sounding out well-known singers who were completely washed up in England. This was a delicate task. Fragile egos were involved and grown men had to be talked to like children. Joining a showband in Ireland was all too accurately perceived as the death rattle of any self-respecting English singer's career.

However, the world being the way it is, we duly received a shortlist of volunteers who were willing to bite the bullet for the sake of a month or two of recaptured glory and a few quid.

We received photographs, curricula vitae and copies of records they had made. Most were one-hit wonders who all looked and sounded more or less the same. There was only one thing to do. During a ceremony, which I witnessed but was too much of a latecomer in the band fully to appreciate, the names were placed in a real hat—a borrowed trilby, as I recall. A hand snaked over the brim and a name emerged.

Hello, Ricky Valance!

Ricky turned out to be a rather dazed Welshman who'd had a Number One hit in 1960 with a timely cover version of a song that had already been a Number One hit in America for a singer called Ray Peterson. The song was called 'Tell Laura I Love Her', a teary, dreary chronicle of events that led to the premature death of a fictional young biker who deserved to have been killed much sooner. A shade on the funereal side for a pop song, it had nevertheless worked its juju and topped the charts. It was the last Ricky was to see of the Number-One slot. He was never destined to sniff the charts again. Joining our band was but one of a series of bruising disappointments. He was duly ferried over and brought to meet the band at rehearsal in a run-down ballroom in the Dublin suburb of Clondalkin (then regarded as being deep in the country) and given a basket of chicken and chips. It was obvious that he was less than enamoured by almost everything he saw and heard (and ate), and I don't suppose we made things particularly easy for him. We disliked him immediately. He seemed much older than we were, even though he was of but twenty-six summers. We weren't so far behind (in our early twenties) but he gave the impression of being from an entirely different generation. And in many ways he was. He was a product of a gentler time, still adhering to traditional show-business values. In attitude, there was little difference between him and the likes of Dickie Valentine, Ronnie Hilton, Max Bygraves or any of the old singer-cum-soft-shoe shufflers. But the world had moved on. The Beatles and The Stones were king. Non-conformity, individuality and ignorance was all. Ricky had been left behind, but didn't know it.

He dressed like my father would have if my father had been given half a chance and a few quid. Formal overcoat, buttoned, flat lapels; stiff charcoal-grey suit a little teddy-boyish below the belt; highly polished winkle-picker shoes and an unnaturally neat head of short oiled hair that stopped just short of a pompadour (his tonsorial arrangement gave the impression that his hair was trying to pump up a head of steam); a round moon-face that showed little sign of expression or of having been lived in at all, and a pair of small, darting eyes placed a little too close together. I noticed that he walked like Elvis. This was not an affected gait. Like Presley, Ricky was pigeon-toed and therefore, just like Elvis, walked the Indian Way. Check out the Indian scout on the hunt for the white man's tracks when you next go to a well-made or reasonably authentic cowboy movie. If the brave portrayed is a genuine Indian, chances are he'll walk with his feet pointed inwards too.

Elvis was sensitive about his Indian Walk (in his movies, it is rare to see a full-length shot of Elvis walking towards camera. When such a shot in unavoidable, he is clearly uncomfortable). Sensitive, too, because of widespread cracker-barrel talk that he really had a drop or two of not-entirely-welcome Indian blood pounding through his veins (whereas, in actual fact, he was rumoured to be more of an Ulster Scot). I don't suppose Ricky could claim the same. Cherokee bucks rarely spent quality time roaming the Welsh valleys.

Suffice to say that Ricky treated us like something he had just scraped from the sole of his shoe but we expected that. The nature of his situation demanded that he put on a show of superiority. He could never be just one of the lads. He knew that. So did we.

Rehearsals proved difficult. He turned out to have a 'throat'.

That's when I knew that he and the land of Erin would never pair. The unhealthy grind of showband life has little tolerance for the weak. Any potential physical frailty shows itself early, is cruelly exposed and roundly punished. Only the healthy and robust can survive for long the travelling, the sitting doing nothing, the bad food, no food, lack of sleep, too much sleep, standing on stage for five hours blowing a trumpet in a sea of cigarette smoke, encounters with venereal travelling girls, suicidal driving by drunken roadies, faulty wiring leading to electrocution in marquees, faulty wiring leading to electrocution in church halls, slithering along frosty roads with no functioning heater, dance-hall germs, the annual monsoons, plague-ridden chip vans, mud baths, poteen from the hills, lung cancer and lack of cigarettes.

Ricky didn't smoke or drink. But he immediately developed a streptococcal throat.

We soon learnt that he was incapable of having a throat that was merely sore, it had to be streptococcal. I couldn't even pronounce it.

This was the way his mind worked. Everything was more serious than it appeared. If he grazed a leg, the wound was potentially gangrenous, every headache heralded a tumour, every shaving nick a haemorrhage and every toothache a terminal abscess.

He was a pain in the coccyx.

Our first task was to sell Ricky to the public. This required the generation of some high-octane publicity. To this end we carefully chose a suitable venue at which we would introduce Ricky to an apathetic public.

We discovered that we would soon be playing support to The Move ('Flowers in the Rain', 'Blackberry Way', etc.) at the Top Hat Ballroom in Lisburn, Co. Down. I knew the venue well. After all, I had fainted there once. It was sweaty and claustrophobic with a low ceiling. Come to think of it, that's why I'd fainted. It was perfect for the building-up of a little hysteria.

All seemed to be slotting nicely into place. A regularly charting English group, well-supported and received with rapture by a young, clued-in Northern crowd would provide cover and an excellent opportunity to generate eminently usable publicity photographs.

Alas, a little duplicity was necessary. We had engaged the services of a photographer called Dave Robinson, a jovial though strange young man who sported a spectacular Afro haircut. Dave's was the first Afro to reach Dublin and consequently much remarked upon. So odd was the tonsorial architecture of his head that it seemed to wrongfoot the normally ever-vigilant smart arses in Dublin who were usually quick to confer clever nicknames. The best they could come up with was the lame 'Hairhead.' But the world was to hear more of Hairhead. He eventually threw his camera away, all the better to achieve fame as the man who founded Stiff Records, a company that introduced to the world a better class of punk—Nick Lowe, Ian Dury and the Blockheads, Wreckless Eric and Jona Lewie.

He, of course, being somewhat of a progressive thinker, summed up the situation expertly and suggested bribing a number of young women (ten shillings a head as I recall) to position themselves in front of the band. At a given cue they would scream and drag Ricky from the stage. Thus would we be the proud owners of fine schnapps of a star being mobbed and manhandled by the many crazed fans surging to get near him.

The Top Hat crowd would, of course, have paid good money to see The Move and wouldn't care much about Ricky Valance or The

Chessmen. As usual, we would kick off the proceedings and labour in the vineyard until we reached that stage of the evening when 'The Move' were ready to take the stage. And we knew that, human nature being what it is, the bulk of the punters would drift towards the stage about fifteen minutes before the star act was due to appear. As the long-awaited moment drew near, we could discern the first traces of the usual frenzy, a frisson of anticipation as each sweaty individual on the floor jostled for pole position to ogle famous tight-crotched English popsters.

Soon they were twenty deep in front of us, a mass of reeking humanity heaving and swaying as one.

The Move, of course, despite their widespread reputation as a hell-raising, drum-kit-destroying, guitar-smashing, drugged-out, fast-living, nonconformist bunch of vicious hedonistic bastards in the company of whom no grown woman or female child was safe, were, in the meantime, sitting quietly backstage sipping tea, chatting amiably about the immediate geographical area to a bulky woman who had brewed up for them and provided a number of thin biscuits.

Our idea was to introduce Ricky approximately five minutes before The Move appeared. The crowd would be suitably fired up by then, simultaneously shouting for the Big Group whilst imploring us to vamoose. Fortunately, from a purely photographic point of view, images of a crowd screaming for an English pop group to materialise tend to look much the same as shots of a crowd screaming at The Chessmen to get off the fucking stage.

Ricky was duly introduced and launched into 'Tell Laura I Love Her', clutching his throat every now and again. The crowd were mainly indifferent, preferring to chant 'We Want The Move!'

All this changed when, at a prearranged signal from Hairhead, the screams of teenage girls rent the air and twenty pairs of grasping hands reached from the body of the crowd, snaked round Ricky's smaller-than-average turned-in feet, ankles and lower calves, and dragged him to the floor accompanied by frequent flashes of a Nikon camera.

The rest of the crowd joined in, surging towards him like sharks in a feeding frenzy. Hairhead's work was done. The schnapps were in the can. We would plant them in the showband rag *Spotlight*—'Singing Sensation Valance Mobbed Up North! Move Fucked!' We could see the headlines already.

Ricky swiftly regained his composure and fought his way back on stage to complete 'Tell Laura I Love Her.' He appeared stunned by this unprecedented display of enthusiasm. He shot nervous darting little glances to the rest of the band and managed to exit stage left, adjusting his tousled hair with a small pocket comb that had suddenly appeared in the palm of his hand. His face was glowing and the eyes had a wildness about them—like a horse after a taxing gallop.

As he passed me on the way to the wings, I thought for a moment that he looked angry.

'Jesus!' he muttered. Then he smiled broadly. 'It's facking happening again!'

I hadn't the heart to tell him.

———

As predicted, Ricky Valance wasn't made for Ireland or the Irish. Although loyally Welsh, there seemed little of the Celt in him. He was serious, fussy and pedantic. There was no sign of craic in him at all—a dull man by nature.

During his sojourn with us, his sense of humour was often rigorously tested.

He was not best pleased when a passing dancer once grabbed his crotch halfway through Englebert Humperdinck's 'Ten Guitars.'

Ricky had been with the band for nearly a fortnight and had already had just about enough of everything. He wasn't accustomed to hanging his clothes on a rusty nail and had rapidly learnt to say no when offered a plate of curled hang sangwidges.

His crotch was interfered with in Glenfarne, Co. Cavan, the original, self-styled 'Ballroom of Romance,' or so said the sign outside on the hall. Old-style ballrooms were usually anonymous, stern places, not usually given or prone to shows of ostentation or flashes of humour when it came to advertising what they had to offer.

I was aware of only one other dance hall in Ireland that made any manner of public claim about the unique allure of their premises. That was Caproni's Ballroom in Bangor, Co. Down. Above the entrance door could be read, in large capitals, THROUGH THESE PORTALS, FROM TIME TO TIME, PASS SOME OF THE MOST BEAUTIFUL GIRLS IN THE WORLD.

Always scanned a mite careful to me—a lack of confidence in the pulchritude of local female talent—might as be well interpreted as, 'Through these portals sometimes pass some of the most beautiful girls in the world, but maybe not tonight.'

Say what you mean or shut the fuck up, I say.

Anyway, Ricky Valance was violated by a red-haired man with a very large nose who had glided by the front of the stage. He was dancing with a short, corpulent women who dragged behind her an almost perfect specimen of the rural dropped arse. As a connoisseur, I found myself marvelling at the perfectly irregular stumpy contours of this remarkable hanging arse—along the lines of the Hottentot Venus. The dropped arse is most often spotted in the west and north-western regions of our island. I'm sure there are sound genetic reasons for this and I'm sure the Moors (via the Hottentots perhaps) come into it somewhere but I must not permit the anthropologist in me to gain the upper hand. Many everyday folk don't care to be referred to as hominids.

Dropped-arse Syndrome is more noticeable in the female of the species on the grounds that the male can better disguise or conceal his low-slung posterior by means of an ill-fitting suit. Men are just as likely to inherit these unfortunate arses as women, in much the same way as an equal percentage of men and women are homosexual, except that most of the women keep it to themselves (to the bitter disappointment of most straight men). However, women, unable to wear cheaply put-together Burton suits, are unavoidably obliged to flash some of their goods. The Syndrome occurs when the upper part of the arse in question begins to form just below the hip-bone (or haunch) but, due to some mischievous directive from God or whoever it is who decides what we look like, ends somewhere just short of the rear of the knee. The area where the arse should normally be is occupied by a flat featureless plateau of flesh, necessitating a natural but cruelly elongated spine. The worst-case scenario (by no means unusual) often occurs in Donegal when a dropped-arsed woman is stricken by the equally distressful Inverted-leg Syndrome. This occurs when the upper part of the leg is worn below the knee. Also genetic, this unfortunate double-whammy leaves the patient with a dropped arse seemingly propped up by legs thick enough to shock Hannibal himself.

But I digress.

With Ricky warbling comfortably, the rogue man, acting presumably on a sudden dark whim, reached up and expertly grabbed Ricky by the balls. A quick squeeze and he was gone.

Ricky wasn't expecting this. He reared back like a stuck pig, then straightened up and glowered at the two highly amused dancers as they spun across the floor unconcerned, the red-haired man shooting the violated singer a wide grin and a friendly thumbs-up.

I edged closer to Ricky and manoeuvred myself in such a way as to stop him from leaping from the stage and doing something stupid.

I grabbed his arm. 'Don't! I said.

'Nobody grabs my balls,' he hissed.

I explained to him that I'd seen the unauthorised grasping of musicians' scrotums before, having once been present at a performance given by a hot showband of the time called The Magnificent Seven. The band hailed from Derry but nonetheless managed to come across as urbane and modern. The gig, in the Pallidrome Ballroom in the restless town of Strabane in Co. Tyrone, was going well.

The build-up to the band's *pièce-de-resistance* necessitated a short break, after which the lead guitarist, rhythm guitarist, bassist and drummer returned with an American swagger, wearing gold lamé jackets, canary yellow trousers and sunglasses (the latter vital for the purpose of conveying to a sun-starved audience an aura of teenage rebelliousness, impossible glamour, and a timely warning concerning the dangers of exposing the naked eye to direct sunlight). They then launched into their tiresome Shadows' act, kicking off with a reasonably accurate version of 'Apache', illustrated by a closely choreographed dance routine. Legs were raised as one and flung casually in synchronisation to the left or right, heads shook in unison, and necks of guitars simultaneously thrust skyward. It was triumph of discipline and order. The tempo was ratcheted up for the second number ('Guitar Boogie Shuffle,' as I recall).

During one of this instrumental's frequent climaxes, the guitar player dramatically spread his legs and fell heavily, and no doubt painfully, upon his knees. Still playing relatively complicated guitar, he leaned backwards alarmingly, contorting his upper torso until the back of his greasy head almost touched the floor behind, a foolhardy move that left him vulnerable at the fork—his stretched satin-encased crotch thrusting aggressively forward, proving a matter of considerable interest to the younger ladies present, many of whose eyes zoomed in hungrily on the clear outline of his substantial cock.

The straining guitarist was destined not to see another face, a face that belonged to a young man whose head was roughly level with the guitarist's strained loins. With what can only be described as a mad screech of either triumph or pent-up frustration, the man extended a hoary hand, took rough purchase on the guitarist testicles and twisted the ball-bag violently.

The guitarist screamed, probably more in surprise than in pain, and collapsed like a tinker's tent. When he'd regained the perpendicular and his composure, he realised that the incident had elicited a huge round of good-natured applause.

Can't fight that. Show business diktat: 'If it works, don't knock it.'

He gathered himself, bowed graciously in acknowledgement, put aside thoughts of revenge, and resumed his pyrotechnics on the next parcel of noise.

There was no point in complaining about a little public ball-twisting if it went down well with the punters. It's quite possible that some of them thought it part of the act.

Ricky didn't understand this.

'I'll kill that facker,' he muttered, scanning the crowd for the male half of the couple, who had conveniently disappeared.

'Let it go,' I whispered. 'Remember where you are. This is a town that may not care for English people. Your ancestors have abused them in the past. There may not be many people here but, believe me, none of them will be on your side. Smile and take it.'

'But I'm fucking Welsh,' he said.

'Same difference.'

He smiled and accepted the unauthorised handling of his reproductive organs. It wasn't a comfortable decision.

To his credit, he realised that he was not dealing with a particularly sophisticated audience. Any mixed-sex gathering of people assembled in a public place who appreciated and positively encouraged the tweaking of an artist's scrotum by a passing stranger must not be regarded as overly refined.

But sometimes the reaction of such an audience is surprising. As I look across at Eddie I recall a moment when the credulity of even The Chessmen was taxed.

It happened one summer's night in the Stardust Ballroom in Cork City. For some reason, not easily understood, The Chessmen had been relatively popular there in the past. We normally went onstage at eleven o'clock which meant we had a few hours to kill. We'd spent a long day travelling and were tired, unenthusiastic at the prospect of the gig ahead.

I sneaked off and went to the movies alone where I promptly fell asleep, somehow arriving back in time to smarten myself up and change into gaudy clothes. By this stage the popularity of The Chessmen was well on the wane and the crowd's reaction decidedly apathetic.

We sleepwalked through an hour. The dance was scheduled to finish at one o'clock. At least the night would be mercifully short.

Between numbers I became aware of something amiss with Eddie. He was leaning on his amplifier, a pained expression on his face.

'What's wrong?' I asked.

'Dying for a Jimmy Riddle,' he answered, squeezing the words out with a degree of effort which did not become him.

'How bad is it?'

'Couldn't be worse,' he grunted, attempting to cross his legs. 'I'm gonna pish meself.'

I felt for him. It wasn't done to leave the stage for a piss—ostensibly a sackable offence. Another old show-business rule, religiously adhered to. And understandable, too, in the greater scheme of things. If heads could leave the stage for a piss everybody would be pissed going on. It was only ignored by bands bereft of hope. We hadn't reached that stage yet, though we were swiftly getting there.

'Pints?' I enquired.

'Yeah.'

Stupid cunt. Served him right. He knew the rules. As far as The Chessmen were concerned, a few shorts only before the gig—straight, no mixers.

'I'm going for a pish.'

'You can't.'

I looked over at the band leader. He hadn't noticed anything amiss. He was reaching for the microphone to announce the next number. It was 'Sabre Dance.'

Eddie's face fell. 'Sabre Dance' was his guitar feature, his showpiece, a whirling, dizzying galaxy of notes performed by the diminutive plank-spanker with much brio and showmanship.

'Bastard!' hissed Eddie.

'Don't blame him. He doesn't know you're hefted. Too late now.'

I was enjoying this.

'Go get 'em, Ed,' I chortled.

'Fuck off!'

The thunderous drum intro to 'Sabre Dance' kicked in.

True professional that he was, Eddie staggered painfully to centre stage, crossed his legs grimly and went into his act, which, as always, mainly consisted of making the playing of the tune look difficult.

The piece was literally a showstopper, chiefly because the dancing punters shuddered to a halt, confused and angered by the frequent tempo changes. They reacted like harassed cattle and stood still, scared, confused and bunched on the dance floor, staring at the stage on the assumption that something had gone wrong.

Eddie made it halfway through the piece before he snapped. With a bellow of anguish, he whipped the guitar from his neck, flung the instrument onto the floor and stomped off stage, presumably to relieve himself against the nearest wall or convenient doorway. His guitar, of course, was still live. The jolt of the instrument crashing to the floor had jangled the strings considerably, producing unearthly scrunching sounds, squealing, wailing and ear-piercing feedback that verged on the unbearable. We had little choice but to continue playing amidst this electronic malfunction and, indeed, I tried to utilise my boot in a vain attempt to unhook Eddie's guitar lead from its socket. Then I noticed that the punters were surging forward, engaged by what was going on and seemingly regarding Eddie's disappearance as part of the act.

OK, I thought, let's ride this bugger out and see where it goes. By this time the unattended guitar, powered by its own vibrations, was actually making its way independently across the wooden boards, writhing snakelike towards the lip of the stage.

Fuck me! I thought. It's heading straight for the punters! Attaboy, Fender! Go get the bastards!

The noise was unbearable by now, severely straining our speakers. Eddie appeared back on stage, snatched the guitar from the ground, and resumed where he'd left off pre-piss.

When the number ground to a halt, we heard something that we hadn't heard for quite some time, the heady sound of approval—wild cheering coupled with thunderous applause.

Eddie bowed gracefully and resumed his normal position next to me.

'What's going on?' he rasped. 'I'm bringing the house down here.'

'Don't worry,' I said. 'They applaud not for you. They're applauding the fucking Electricity Board.'

We had learnt another valuable show-business lesson.

It is possible to be more popular by not being onstage than by being on it so we may as well piss when we feel like it.

Morality Tale
Show Business Lesson Number One
Never Assume That Popularity Equates With Wealth

There is a pub in Harry Street called Bruxelles. Outside stands a statue of the late Phil Lynott, he of Thin Lizzy fame. The statue stands outside Bruxelles because the establishment used to be known as the Zodiac Bar, the basement section of which had served as the regular weekly haunt of showband heads and rockers alike, including the same Phil. During the early seventies, the two species mingled freely before the onset of demarcation, which roughly coincided with the spawning of U2 and their reading of Bibles in dingy dressing rooms. None was more genial than Phil himself, who enjoyed a pint every bit as much as the showband chancers standing beside him.

It was a happy, uncomplicated time. We hadn't yet learned to despise each other. That came later with marketing…and the bibles.

In 1973 Phil Lynott and Thin Lizzy burst onto the English pop charts with a spruced-up version of 'Whiskey in the Jar.' In a Dublin so unsure of itself that anything even vaguely English was regarded as superior to anything we could produce ourselves, such recognition for something indigenous was unprecedented, the ultimate achievement.

Showbands, of course, had already made an impact of sorts on the English charts. But nothing to be proud of. *Basso profundo* Larry Cunningham's sleepy 'Tribute to Jim Reeves', the late-but-screaming Joe Dolan's 'Make Me an Island' and semi-comatose Frankie McBride's 'Five Little Fingers' had all charted with varying degrees of success. Even blameless Dana was Number One for a while after she won the Eurovision Song Contest with 'All Kinds of Everything.' But none of this seemed to count, mainly because we regarded these efforts as pieces of shite.

To us, in our naivety, Phil's 'Whiskey in the Jar' was real rock 'n' roll, with a touch of the undistilled proud Paddy thrown in there for good measure. It was real, note-perfect and noteworthy—a breakthrough. Well, that's what we thought at the time. We knew no better. These distinctions seemed important.

Consequently, when Phil showed up in the Zodiac one Monday night after appearing on *Top of the Pops* the week before, he was a conquering hero. Like Val Doonican in Shorrocks.

Heaven knows what the English made of Phil when he opened his mouth to speak. He spoke like the earthy Dub that he was and didn't look like any Irish person they had ever seen. He wasn't particularly handsome, the too-long equine face and jutting jaw put paid to that. What he did have was a personality, which was enough to be going on with when we factor in the glowing copper skin, the aerodynamically sound Afro (this was post-Hairhead), the twinkle in the eye, the lounge-lizard pencil-thin moustache, the rangy frame, the clinging leather and the high-heeled boots. I once saw a gay man actually physically swoon at the sight of him. But that wasn't Phil's fault. He was what he was—a charver magnet—the face of the Ireland to come—in appearance, a cross between Randolph Turpin and Samuel Beckett.

Every musician there wanted to be Phil for a day, on the prior assumption that twenty-four hours would be more than long enough to be black.

Drink flowed, backs were slapped and a good time was had all round. All went well until I found myself in the cramped toilet having a piss.

Phil Lynott came in for the same purpose.

I knew him well enough and congratulated him on his success across the Sheugh.

He looked over his shoulder nervously, checking the door.

"Do me a favour, head?' he whispered, from the corner of his mouth, in which was also lodged the remains of a Benson and Hedge.

'No problem. Shoot,' I replied.

'Could you lend me a tenner?'

He checked the door again.

'Fuck off!' I replied, thinking he was joking.

'No,' he said. 'I'm serious.'

I realised he was and slipped him a tenner.

He smiled as he left. 'Now I can buy somebody a drink,' he smiled. 'Things are never what they're cracked up to be, head.'

Then he was gone.

Ah, the inherent ugliness of show business again. There must be no greater hell than that which obliges a now-famous pop star (the idol of his peers, the author of a breakthrough, trailblazer rock 'n' roll record) to panhandle in the jacks.

I met him but once more, a month or so before he died in 1986. Professionally, he was on his last legs but, I thought, holding up pretty well physically. He looked good but was merely going through the motions, playing for a meagre and unimpressed crowd at the Rialto Cinema in Derry with a band that he knew wasn't any good. It was a sad occasion and I felt sorry for him. Thus do our gods gradually disassemble. Nevertheless, although he was probably quite wealthy by then, I'm sure he would've settled for being broke and famous in the Zodiac.

I didn't mention the tenner.

Rare is the man amongst us who can idly gaze at the guano-spattered statue of someone who still owes him money.

We generally looked forward to a Monday. That was the one dependable day off for most of the heads. Very few bands were called upon to play a gig on that night unless it happened to be at the Television Club in Harcourt Street, a prestigious booking for the outfit concerned, if only because it provided one of the few opportunities to be heard by one's musical peers. Unfortunately, one's peers spent most of their time pissed in the balcony bar chasing or, alternatively, avoiding women from the country.

I went there most Monday nights, but there was another Monday gig in town that was less popular. It was where the Old Heads could be heard.

The music scene was changing rapidly. By the late sixties there were three broad categories of musicians. The show-band boom was ephemeral by nature, a carpetbagger's business, a set of unique circumstances that had created a brief opportunity for cover bands to make a lot of money for a short time. Most of the show-band musicians were chancers and well aware of it. But there was another generation of musicians still very much active. These were the older heads who had played in sit-down bands and orchestras that flourished up until the late fifties. Many of them were brass players and now eked out a living as best they could, playing in jazz pubs and as session musicians.

And then there were the Young Turks, the rockers. The likes of Skid Row and Thin Lizzy would point the way to U2 and their eventual conquest of the music world.

So there was us, the Old Heads and the Young Turks. The three co-existed uneasily.

I had no strong opinions one way or the other and found it difficult to take the music business seriously. But although I liked most of the Young Turks (apart from the occasional arsehole like Gary Moore) and could see where they were headed, I, for some reason which I have yet to fathom, was more interested in the lost world of the Old Heads, many of whom were extremely angry at the cruel hand life had dealt them.

I had a grudging respect for them, even though they were, on the whole, a miserable shower of bastards.

I first came across them in recording studios when we were occasionally herded in to cover some American or British group's record in the faint hope that our inferior but similar version would somehow be preferred to the original. It never was.

There is no more depressing sight in this world than a jaded bunch of hard-bitten, pipe-smoking session musicians slumped in their plastic chairs, willing the clock to race faster towards quitting time whilst they fabricate reasons to delay the moment when they have to actually lift their instruments and play a note or two. They were usually to be found manning drums, piano, trumpet, trombone, saxophone, or the occasional double bass. At the risk of being unkind to them, they were like knackered elephants waiting for the cue to shuffle off to the bone-yard. Whatever inner fire had sparked them to take up music in the first place had long since been extinguished, converting them into cynical, dead-eyed, union-book-waving, cardigan-clad, tweedy wankers.

Maybe I would've been like them, had I been one of them. I like to think I would have been different. I have always been aware of the Golden Rule of Music, i.e. the type of music that inspires one to take up a musical instrument will automatically become unpopular and obsolete by the time one feels one has mastered it. This tends to co-incide with one's thirtieth birthday.

These Old Heads spent much time lamenting the passing of orchestras and dance bands that played 'real' music. They had little or no time for pimply young fuckers with guitars who required the occasional toot of a trumpet or squeak of a saxophone to flesh out their nursery-rhyme pop songs. These bored session musicians treated us young 'uns with open contempt.

They were absolutely right to do so, of course, and I do remember feeling a degree of sympathy for them but they were difficult, ornery bastards and hard to like. A noble disdain on their part would've been quite sufficient.

There was a unique and concentrated nest of Old Heads to be seen and heard on a Monday night. The last remaining proper sit-down res-ident orchestra in Ireland played nightly in the ballroom above Clery's department store in O'Connell Street.

Ascending Clery's stairs to the ballroom was like climbing up to the Land that Time Forgot—some plateau on a mountaintop, undisturbed by modern life, an environment conducive to the preservation and pro-tection of species extinct elsewhere.

Amid Old Worlde opulence and a dangerously polished dance floor jutted a stage manned by fifteen men in dinner suits and bow-ties. There were usually more people onstage than in the rest of the room.

The sprinkling of people who did attend consisted of shabby men, a fair proportion of whom were wearing cheap wigs, and women of a certain age who wore too much make-up and were supported by the mandatory scrawny hooker's legs.

I would attend maybe one Monday in four. It was a solitary ritual. I could never talk anyone into coming with me. The more I told them what to expect, the less they seemed inclined to go. I felt like a bird-watcher or trainspotter—an anorak.

The band's routine never varied. Dancing hours were from nine p.m. until two a.m.—with the same songs performed at approximately the same time each night, to the extent that the opening bars of 'Sentimental Journey' signified that it was exactly five minutes to midnight.

I enjoyed soaking up the invigorating air of despair and hopeless-ness. The bandleader wore shabby tails and conducted the band with a baton to which none of the musicians paid the slightest attention. His hair was Brylcreemed, parted down the middle and I seem to remember a small killer moustache.

He spent the bulk of his time staring fixedly at the undisturbed floorboards wearing a permanent oily grin, similar to that often resident on the faces of circus ringmasters.

The mask would drop only if he heard an errant honk, rogue squeak or imperfect plink from the depths of the orchestra, but, other than cast a swift, dark, dirty look at the culprit on these admittedly rare occasions, he remained generally serene. Almost avuncular.

I often wondered what thoughts passed through his head during the long, grinding hours of sparsely supported foxtrots, sambas and quicksteps. It's not easy to smile at fuck-all for five straight hours. Such a feat requires rare dedication. Try it some time.

However, he did have a habit that endeared him to me and, no doubt, to others of a similar frame of mind. Just before the last number of the evening, when the alcohol had faded in the bloodstreams of the musicians and they were semi-catatonic due to advanced *ennui*, he would face the tiny audience, extract a gold pocket watch from the vicinity of his cummerbund, hold it high in the air, peer at it shortsightedly and turn theatrically to the band.

'My!' he would exclaim. 'It's five minutes to two o'clock. Wherever does the time go?'

What cruelty and irony. And what an undoubted touch of class.

——

But most Monday nights I went to the Television Club. All heads were to be found there on the day succeeding the Sabbath. This ballroom (which also housed the Eamonn Andrews Recording Studios) was situated on Harcourt Street and fit for the purpose of clearing house for false promises. The main attraction was that it acted as the charver epicentre of the showband world, a place where women encountered on the road were encouraged to seek us out on a Monday night 'if you're ever in Dublin'.

Consequently, one never knew who was likely to show up. Invitations to rendezvous in the TV Club were issued for a variety of reasons. One might very well have met a genuinely nice young lady in Cahirciveen and issued the invite in good faith. Or, as was more likely the case, it was a gruff post-coital parting shot whispered in the Stygian gloom of the alleyway behind the breezeblock behemoth that was the venue in Castleblayney, accompanied by a hurried re-adjustment of clothing, further hastened by the impatient hooting horn of the waiting coach.

Usually, though, apart from the usual local clientele, only the Woodentops would show up amongst the regular Dublin selection of available flesh. Every band had its Woodentops, girls who, for reasons probably only partially understood by themselves, would pledge their allegiance to one band and one band only… for a finite period of time…

Woodentops did not consider themselves 'groupies' in the accepted sense of the word i.e. girls who would allow themselves to be fucked by any musician who cared to bother. No, Woodentops were faithful to one band and looked towards no other. Woodentops were true, except when they switched their allegiance to another set of musicians, which often happened, the point being that they were true to one band *at a time*. Until the moment they decided to jump ship, they considered themselves to be ours and ours alone. It was the closest they might ever get to the concept of monogamy.

Our Woodentops were Anne and Phyllis (names changed to protect the guilty), lookalike sisters from Sligo. The origin of their sobriquet could be discerned piled on top of their skulls—two mammoth beehives of hair lacquered to the extent that they reminded the Egyptologists amongst us of concrete Pharaoh's hats. They were alternatively known as Jekyll and Hyde (rhyming slang. Work it out) due to their loose grasp of sexual morality.

They came to every gig we played within a fifty-mile radius of Sligo, always cheerful, always primitively radiant. We had used them shamefully and carnally at the start, but the novelty soon faded. Even Lashback couldn't be bothered with them any more, the significance of which should have triggered alarm bells in their communal brains

Last time I saw either Woodentop had been in a crumbling hotel room in Bundoran. I had snapped awake to a blinding headache, not helped by beams of unbearably bright sunlight boring into my squinting eyes.

Flailing my arms in panic at this sudden awakening in harsh circumstances, I made contact with the top of the skull of an undeniably female form lying beside me. By the crisp, crackling sound made by the woman's hair when struck by my recklessly flung limb, and by the shrill oath uttered in reaction to the blow, I realised that I was in bed with a Woodentop.

As Woodentops do, she recovered quickly and switched to automatic pilot, which in her case involved grabbing my exposed crotch and making little cooing sounds.

Alas, my ardour had cooled. Last night had been one thing, the jarring reality of this early sighting of a Woodentop quite another. Woodentops are seldom at their best first thing in the morning. Smudged mascara aside, there were great cracks in her pancake facial make-up, and a chance glance revealed that the services of a hammer and chisel might be required if ever she decided to chip away the layered deposits of talcum powder that had calcified in her armpits.

'Which one are you?' I croaked, clamping her wrist with a restraining hand.

'Phyllis,' she answered, sleepily.

'Where's the other one?'

'Dunno.'

I hoped she wasn't lurking in the room. I remembered little about the night before.

Phyllis rallied suddenly and threw her leg over me like a steeplechase jockey, adopting a sitting position on top of me which enabled her to slowly grind her moist crotch against mine whilst simultaneously craning forward, slowly but expertly trailing erect nipples across my chest. She was particularly proud of them. I once heard her proudly announce to mixed company that her nipples were like six-inch nails.

My head pounded and my tongue stuck to the roof of my mouth.

'Fuck off!' I cried. I shook her off and crawled out of bed.

'You told me last night that you loved me,' she whimpered.

I found her crumpled dress on the floor and handed it to her—an obvious hint. It was her only item of clothing bar a pair of white high-heeled shoes. Woodentops generally travelled light.

'O'Brien wanted me last night, you know,' she sniffed.

Don't flatter yourself, I thought. It wasn't you he was after. I looked across the room and saw again the large hole in the door. One of the stout wooden panels had been riven in by the might of a human fist. Remnants of moist foam clung to the soggy carpet.

Now I remembered.

Mike O'Brien had done his Clockwork Orange again.

The movie of the same name had had a profound effect upon him. *Clockwork Orange*, inspired by the book written by Anthony Burgess when he thought he was dying but wasn't, featured a futuristic, sadistically violent gang called the Droogs who, inspired by the music of Beethoven and partially choreographed by Gene Kelly's 'Singin' In The Rain', attacked and sometimes killed people for no particular reason.

After seeing the film dozens of times, Mike took to carrying a holdall. This contained his Droog Suit i.e. black bowler hat, cricketer's jockstrap, elongated phallic nose, braces, white granddad shirt, tight white trousers, black leather boots, collapsible cane with mock-silver knob on top and a small cassette player. Everywhere he went, the holdall was sure to go.

He didn't use the contents often. Maybe once every three or four weeks. But when he did, the consequences were severe. Nobody knew what triggered the action. We would try to second-guess him but never managed to crack it.

The Drooging would invariably occur in hotels between the hours of four and five a.m. when all was still. One victim only was selected.

Picture this.

The prey would lie alone in bed (or accompanied, as the case may be. It mattered not to O'Brien), asleep. He would be jerked into semi-consciousness by the splintering crash of his hotel room door being kicked in. He would snap fully awake and become aware of the distorted, tinny screech of a section of Beethoven's Ninth Symphony emanating at full volume from a straining, inadequate, cassette machine. He would rub his eyes and behold the spectre of a shadowy white-clad, bowler-hatted figure with a protruding nose approaching his bed, holding aloft a large metal canister.

The groggy victim would instinctively fear for his life but his screams would be smothered as the fire extinguisher was activated and both occupant and bed would instantly be engulfed in evil-smelling foam. The victim would claw at his own rapidly-constricting throat and through stinging eyeballs catch but a passing glimpse of the nightmarish figure retreating into the night.

He'd been Drooged.

Next day, none of this would be mentioned.

Staying in small hotels equipped with fire extinguishers was considered an occupational hazard. O'Brien would behave quite normally when morning broke. As if nothing were amiss. The victim would clean himself up and tidy his room as best he could.

Oddly, I had heard him coming last night. I was lying in bed drunk whilst the Woodentop was noisily occupied doing something vaguely pleasant in the vicinity of my lower torso.

I was staring at the ceiling when I heard the faint clink of a metallic object outside my door at what seemed an unreasonable hour.

Putting two and two together, I leapt smartly from the jaws of the Woodentop and jammed a heavy table against the door. The Woodentop screamed at the possible implications of such an unexpected and rash act. The tinny telltale snatch of Beethoven's Ninth floated in from the hallway. A heavy shoulder was applied from without but the stout door held fast against the table. A fist pounded the door panelling. Shards of wood flew.

The weakened door panel finally gave way and an arm snaked through the aperture, groping for the doorknob. I administered a crisp karate chop to the limb. The arm sagged and was swiftly withdrawn.

A tapered metal nozzle appeared through the gaping hole in the door and, before I could grasp it and attempt to prevent the flow, a thick jet of pressurized foam shot thickly into the room.

I heard agitated voices from the floor below and the hurried sound of feet climbing stairs. I sensed that O'Brien had now retreated.

I heard a civilised knock upon the door and, then, peering through the jagged hole, stood the manager of the hotel. He was a small, frightened man, timid and unused to trouble. I opened the door slightly but not enough that he might see what had been done to his room in the name of show business. I hid my nakedness with a strategically placed hand.

'In the Name of God are you all right?' he anxiously enquired.

'I'm fine… now,' I said.

'What happened here?' he demanded to know.

'I was attacked,' I replied.

'Did you see who it was?'

'Yes.'

'Can you describe him?'

'Describe him? I know him.'

'You know him?'

'It was one of the lads out of the band. Sleep-walking. He didn't know what he was doing.'

The manager wasn't quite sure how to react. He was scratching his chin now, leaving trails in the shrubbery of his stubble.

'Sleep-walking?'

He was echoing everything I said.

'You're repeating everything I say,' I said.

'Repeating?'

'Please don't hold it against the lad.' I pleaded. 'He suffers from a particularly virulent form of the phenomenon. In the morning he'll have no recollection of what transpired here. We all have crosses to bear, his is just a little heavier than most. He's not a well man.'

The manager lapsed into patois. 'Dere's been damage done to de door dere.'

Luckily he couldn't see the state of the room's interior.

'I'll pay for any damage in the morning. Let's leave it at that.' I thought I sounded noble.

He seemed to accept this and did not object when I eased him away and closed the savaged door.

I comforted the Woodentop and put her back to bed. The foam had spared the bedding. I left everything else as it was and went back to sleep.

The manager eyed me warily in the late morning when I finally surfaced. Other members of the band were scattered about the foyer. Our coach stood outside with Harpo impatient at the wheel. The manager stood behind the front desk of the hotel and fiddled with his watch-chain.

'Sorry about the fracas last night,' I said breezily.

He beckoned me closer.

'Who was it attacked you?' he whispered.

'Can't say. He'll be embarrassed if I reveal his identity. There's a certain amount of sensitivity involved here.'

'I won't let on. I promise.'

'It was O'Brien.'

'Jesus! And he seems so normal. He left earlier this morning. Seemed fine.'

'There you go.'

'There is however,' said the manager, rubbing his nose, 'the small matter of compensation for the door.'

'Right,' sez I.

'We'll have to replace the entire door.'

'How much?'

'Twenty-five pounds,' he looked swiftly away. Guiltily, I thought.

Expensive for a standard door, I thought. Chiselling bastard. No skin off my nose, though. This was coming out of O'Brien's pay packet. Might just cure him of his night romps. Better get out of here before the maid sees the carpet. I had instructed the Woodentop to stay in the room and let nobody in until we'd disappeared over the horizon.

I paid the shrewish manager, obtained a receipt and wandered over to where the rest of lads had gathered.

'What was that door made of,' said Lashback. 'Fucking platinum?'

'Givvus a look at that receipt,' said Eddie.

I handed it to him. He stared at it for a moment.'

'I have to go back upstairs. Won't be long.'

'Don't be all fucking day,' said a hung over Ray.

I lifted my overnight bag and planted it in the coach.

After a smoke and a breath of air, I went back into the hotel to round up the others.

I head a strained oath coming from the direction of the first floor landing just above us. It was Eddie descending the stairs supporting, with some degree of difficulty, my hotel door above his head. He had wrenched it from its hinges.

The manager intercepted Eddie at the foot of the staircase.

'Where are you going with that? It's hotel property.'

Good old Eddie. He was way ahead of me.

'It is not hotel property. Not any more. It belongs to us. That man has a receipt,' Eddie stated with confidence.

'Put that door down or I'll call the Garda Síochána! You can't take a door out of my hotel. Nobody's ever done that before.'

'Excuse me, sir,' sez I. 'You yourself said that the door needs to be replaced in its entirety. The band has paid for a new door. Therefore the old one, *ipso facto*, belongs to us. My colleague is merely carrying out my instructions. We have a receipt. Place the band's door in the van please, Edward, if you will.'

Eddie and the door brushed past.

A screech was heard from above. A Woodentop was hanging over a high banister at some risk to her personal safety.

'Can I leave the room now? Somebody's taken the door.'

'Yes,' I replied. 'Your work is done here.'

The door travelled with us for a number of weeks. It had its own seat. Its presence confused non-members of the band who had cause to enter the vehicle.

I took a degree of pleasure when negotiating Army check-points in the North. No squaddie ever enquired as to what a hotel door was doing in our coach. Maybe they were afraid to hear the answer. They just wanted to go back home. They'd seen too much.

Its novelty eventually wore off and we ceremonially burnt it on the banks of the Boyne just below Slane Castle. Symbolic.

Ray probably appreciated that. It was hard to tell.

13

'Those were the days,' said a wistful Eddie, blowing small but agreeably circular smoke rings towards the roof of the coach.

We were rattling along well. Newry wasn't too far away. See Naples and die. See Newry and Mourne.

The road from Dublin to Belfast was a disgrace. No wonder this country was fucked. At least a decent road between the two capital cities of the island would've been a start. It doesn't seem too much to ask. I blame the North.

Imagine how we must look through the eyes of a foreign tourist (it's easy to spot tourists in Northern Ireland. They're usually the ones wearing real clothes) who rents a car and leaves the city of Belfast en route to Dublin, the latter city being, depending on who the tourist talks to, a bustling, interesting, literary, historic city, or, alternatively, a priest-ridden nest of agitators and vipers whose sole aim in life is to usurp Northern Ireland and disembowel all Protestants.

The tourist driver will find himself driving southwards on the M1 Motorway, which, he might surmise, will take him to Dublin. He would be wrong.

The M1 Motorway was built when money was plentiful, Stormont never had it so good and people knew their place. But herein lay a problem. Any rational person could be forgiven for expecting Northern Ireland to co-operate with the Republic of Ireland in creating a mutually beneficial road link between the two major, and capital, cities of Ireland.

Not a chance.

Our lads Up North weren't having it. They had the money but not the inclination. Hence, our foreign tourist would slip onto the M1 and, after a very few smooth miles, spot an ill-placed and, we sense, begrudged signpost indicating that he must leave the motorway if planning to proceed, as the sign reluctantly indicates, to the South. This grand modern highway sweeps off to the West of Northern Ireland for many miles, avoiding densely populated areas, before finally petering out amongst grazing sheep somewhere not too far from Enniskillen. It seemed manifestly plain that those who designed and built the M1 in the days when Northern Ireland ruled itself preferred this superhighway to go more or less nowhere rather than anywhere near Dublin.

'Ah, those were the days,' Eddie repeated.

'That was only six months ago,' I said.

'Wha?'

'And it's how long since we were in The Chessmen?'

'Nearly a year.'

'Seems longer somehow. Where does the time go?' I ventured.

We both laughed. A short silence developed.

'Things are different now,' sighed Eddie.

And I suppose they were. Or maybe we were just tired. We were living through the dying days of the show-band boom. And the sooner it died the better. Its death would put us out of our misery and force us to do something else for a living, something healthy and constructive perhaps.

'Thank fuck,' I breathed.

'Wha?' said Eddie.

'Oh, nothing,' I answered.' Just talking to myself...'

We went back to staring at the back of Harpo's skull.

His curly head turned slightly towards us and he spoke from the corner of his mouth. He'd been listening to our conversation.

'Tell us the one about the Hammerman,' he said.

'No,' I replied. 'I told it to you before.'

'Tell it again. I like it.'

'Go on,' cajoled Eddie. 'I like it too.'

'It's was true, wasn't it?' enquired Harpo.

'Really happened,' I replied.

They wanted to hear about the Hammerman's Monday routine. When I first arrived in Dublin to join The Chessmen, he was already in the band but, due to a complicated set of circumstances, found himself temporarily homeless. Needless to say, he was from the North too.

We eventually talked our way into the front-room flat of a Victorian house in Anglesey Road, across the street from where Brendan Behan was married. His widow, Beatrice, still lived down the road. I always kept an eye out for her going to the shops. We occupied a bed-sit with two single beds at opposite ends of a large, cold dungeon with a high ceiling. Furniture-wise, apart from a rickety sofa, that was more or less it, apart from a never-to-be-used kitchen of sorts that I found lurking behind a soiled curtain. We soon discovered that we were soul-mates in many ways, both of us settling independently on a fairly restricted diet which consisted of the occasional bag of chips, a surfeit of straight vodka and limitless cigarettes.

On the whole, it didn't matter much where we lived. Constantly travelling, we just needed a place to sleep. Monday was the only complete day off and thus, technically, the only day we used our flat like normal human beings.

Mondays were primarily used for rest and recreation. For Hammerman, this meant sex. He had many willing women on call, of course, but liked a challenge on a Monday.

When the day dawned, he would snap awake at the unusually early jangle of his alarm-clock and, washed, shaved, perfumed, he'd be on the street by ten a.m. I would continue to sleep. It was part of the deal.

Hammerman would home in on the supermarket in Donnybrook, opposite Kiely's pub. Lifting a basket and pretending to shop, he would prowl the aisles.

As Hammerman well knew, all supermarkets then were shuttered and silent on the Sabbath. Therefore, on any given Monday morning, a rich variety of young and not-so-young housewives could be found foraging for essentials.

Let us not underestimate the talent required to entice a young married woman back to a fetid bed-sit on a dreary Monday morning. Particularly a young married woman doing her shopping, the last thought in whose mind would be the likelihood of being talked into being fucked before lunch by a dark-haired stranger whom she met at the canned goods section of her local supermarket.

His was a rare gift that never failed him. And it wasn't that he was particularly handsome. He wasn't. But he had sex appeal and a devastating line of patter. He was the Master. No woman could resist him. I have never trusted a woman since. I figure they must be congenitally powerless when confronted by attractive and persistent evil. They're doomed by their instincts. Helpless in the face of irresistible shite-talk.

My first inkling of his return would be a furtive whispering and the soft clunk of a bag of groceries gently lowered to the floor.

I, of course, had promised to remain fast asleep at all times, permitted only to open the occasional slit of an eye when curiosity got the better of me.

I remember one Monday morning when his prey for the day was particularly young. From what I could make out she seemed barely more than a teenager. I did, however see the flash of a wedding ring. That was all right then. All the boxes were ticked.

The illicit couple duly disrobed and slipped into bed whereby, as per our long-standing prior arrangement, he kicked the sheets from the bed to facilitate my view.

Heavy foreplay ensued and, after a time, he suggested that a little oral sex might not go amiss.

'What'll I do!' she enthusiastically yelped, in an accent not unknown to those who frequented Moore Street before it became the League of Nations.

This was getting good. I had pulled the blankets over my head and could now observe keenly through a small carefully crafted wrinkle in the military blankets.

'Pretend it's a lollipop,' suggested the ever-helpful Hammerman.

She proceeded so to do with commendable application.

She stopped.

'I'd rather have an intercourse,' she piped.

'There'll be plenty of time for that.'

'I've never done this lollipop stuff before.'

'Not even with your husband?'

'He never asked.'

'Takes all sorts.'

'Whaddya mean?'

'Don't you like it?'

'I don't know if I do or not.'

'Well, it doesn't work if you stop.'

I was enjoying this. Hammerman had a live one here. I decided to snore a little. Shake him up a bit.

'Is yer man awake?'

'Naw. Snores like a hippo.' He knew what I was at.

'He's making noises.'

'You've stopped again.' I detected a hint of impatience in Hammerman's voice.

Easy, boy.

'Sorry,' she whimpered.

More slurping sounds.

'What'll happen if I keep doing this?' she gasped.

Hammerman was being sorely tried.

'Stop talking. Keep doing it and you'll find out.'

'Will you have a jackillayshun?'

'With a bit of luck.'

'I've never seen a man having one outside of…you know…'

'Outside of what?'

'My husband has never jackillated outside of my…you know…'

She pointed south towards her crotch.

'What'll happen when you jackillate?'

'What do you mean what'll happen?'

She looked down at his angry organ.

'Will it go BANG?'

That was it.

I fell out of bed.

Harpo was enjoying this. The coach was now travelling too fast. It was excited.

'Slow down a bit,' I demanded.

He eased his foot back from the accelerator pedal.

'What did she do then?' Harpo asked.

'Jumped out of bed and fucked off. Hammerman wasn't best pleased. Best part of it was, she left her groceries behind.'

'And wha?'

'We had a fine breakfast of a bottle of Sasparilla, a tin of pilchards, strawberry jam, a tube of toothpaste and a jumbo bottle of Pine disinfectant.'

We chuckled for a while and grew quiet.

How cruel we were.

Oh, well.

We were near the border now.

———

Nobody in the band was overly keen on visiting the North these days, for entirely different reasons. Billy Brown had the best motive of all for staying out—the real risk of possible arrest and incarceration for non-payment of alimony.

Pat was the most apprehensive, chiefly because the very concepts of widespread disorder, public hatred and displays of mass discontent were alien to him. Not for him the sudden whoosh of the Molotov Cocktail and the heady whiff of cs gas. After all, he was from Arklow, where the chances of being shot by the British Army or mown down by a teenager high on pills were next to nil.

Us Northern boys were hardened to what was going on Up There, and the Dublin contingent, Lashback, Eddie and O'Brien, didn't scare easily.

Pat didn't understand the nature of the problem in the North and, in his innocence, tended to bring the subject up. Attempting to gently discourage him, I would be as kind as my nature allowed and urge him not to concern himself with matters that would only disturb him, chiefly because there was no logic involved.

Others in the band did not share my reluctance to dissect the situation of our brothers in the North.

I was just glad to be out of it. These were testing times. Earlier in the year matters had come to a head on Bloody Sunday in Derry when the cork really had come out of the bottle with the shooting dead of fourteen natives for reasons that were not entirely clear. Thousands had gathered for a march that had been declared illegal by the Northern Ireland Government. I hadn't been there that day, of course, but I'd been to Derry in the interim and had talked to friends who'd been present. Eye witnesses and participants in the march talked of a turkey shoot. It's difficult to dismiss talk like that, especially when it comes from the mouths of the more agile, surviving turkeys.

The whole business reeked of a miscalculation by top Army brass who failed to realise that this was the twentieth century and not the time to teach fuzzy-wuzzies a lesson in front of the television lenses of an increasingly sophisticated media. It smacked of the last kick of a dying Empire doing things the way things had always been done.

My brother was there that day. He was pinned in a doorway for an hour. Bullets thudded off the concrete walls on either side of him. Try telling him that nobody was trying to kill him. He couldn't speak for three days, not accustomed to being pinned down by concentrated rifle fire on his way home for his tea.

But, as usual Up There, in the midst of tragedy there were sparks of the dark humour that tends to separate us from normal mortals. At one stage during the turkey shoot, I was told of a knot of people cowering behind a convenient heap of rubble which was being raked by decidedly unfriendly fire. These men and women were not happy. Being used as target practice by the First Parachute Regiment of the British Army tends to spoil a person's afternoon. One young man cracked under the strain. Overwhelmed by frustration and fuelled by a rush of blood to the head, he burst from his meagre cover and, in an impressive display of bravado, stood alone and cruelly exposed on open ground. He'd had enough. His arms flailed wildly. He was heard to scream, 'Shoot me! Why don't you shoot me as well, you fuckers! What are you waiting for? Shoot us all, why don't you? Ya bastards!'

As he defiantly stood, awaiting the expected bullet in the chest, the rest of the group looked on with some anxiety and a high degree of trepidation.

A small still voice was heard from amongst the huddled would-be targets, a voice directed at the hero.

It whispered, 'Speak for yourself!'

Bloody Sunday upped the ante. In the immediate aftermath of the shootings, the fledgling IRA were pushed to find the manpower required to process the applications of hundreds of angry young men who wanted to fight back. Queues stretched around the block. Many of those young men learnt that joining was the easy part—it was resigning that would prove difficult...

The North is indeed a crazy place.

And so are many of us who live there.

In the coach I needed only to cite the examples Billy, Ray, Harpo and, yes, me.

Looking at those three reminded me that, contrary to popular belief, the Troubles in Northern Ireland had little to do with religious affiliation or dogma. What we were, and still are, dealing with Up There is the clash of two tribes—one nominally Irish, the other nominally

Ulster Scots—the old story of settlers versus indigents, yes, cowboys and Indians. That this sense of difference and aggravated alienation had been allowed to continue and fester for nearly four hundred years is more than unfortunate.

The bald fact remains that most Protestants do not consider themselves Irish whereas most Catholics do.

This is compounded by a long-standing conviction that one group is superior to the other—hence the root of the Troubles.

The importance of the Ulster Scots ingredient in the make-up of all of us born in the North is not fully understood. It's time it was. It's the key to the mess.

I could see the problem from where I lay sprawled in the coach. The former from Ballymena and the other two from Belfast, neither Billy, Ray or Harpo considered themselves Irish. Although nominally descended from good Planter stock, they didn't consider themselves Ulster Scots either (too far in the past), nor did they consider themselves Northern Irish, or British or Ulstermen. They didn't think in terms of nationality. They just thought of themselves as being, well, better than other people, especially better than people from the South.

They assumed that a natural order prevailed. It was not something they thought much about. They regarded their superiority as given, self-evident.

They were not in any way bigoted or racist towards Irish Catholics. They just thought of themselves as different, better—it was a matter of fact. Theirs was an easy, infuriating sense of superiority, born of a confidence rarely encountered in Northern Catholics, or in the pre-Celtic-Tiger Southerner.

And infuriating because a natural confidence and sense of superiority is self-perpetuating in that the being who feels himself superior seldom questions the wisdom of his own convictions. Infuriating also because Billy and Ray in particular were exceptionally good at what they did. Harpo was just wild, but that's a talent too.

I'm not sure if the others realised the extent to which the three lads didn't think about them at all. They didn't seem to catch the little patronising smile, the airy dismissal of a point of view, the reluctance to listen, the dry throwaway remark, the easy contempt, the way Billy tended to treat O'Brien like a child, despite the fact that the latter was extremely bright.

Sometimes I thought Eddie was aware of it but I decided to leave it be. Let the hare sit.

I understood this assumed superiority well because I had a foot in both camps.

My great-grandfather had been a Scottish Presbyterian Minister, my mother a country girl from Donegal who had been hired out at the age of sixteen in 1919.

From the point of view of the purist, and there are many in Northern Ireland, I was neither one or the other. I was a hybrid.

During the late fifties, I was a great fan of Westerns. So was everybody else. We were caught up in the Hollywood hokum. We believed it. A man had to do what a man had to do. I also spent summers with my elderly uncles on the slopes of a barren hill in Donegal. I saw no connection between the two activities. My two uncles were small-scale farmers, albeit without a great degree of enthusiasm.

As I matured I studied them more carefully. I realised that their manner of speech was similar to that used by cowboys in the movies. This surprised me. I couldn't figure it out. But the evidence was there for all to hear. My uncles spoke with a distinct lazy drawl and used words like 'vittles' and 'varmints'. They would routinely 'chaw tobaccy' and speak fondly of 'critturs' (poteen, too, was known as 'the crittur'). Our horse, of whom I was inordinately fond, was not a 'horse' at all. It was a 'hoss'. That's what the cowboys called their horses too. There it was again. What the fuck was going on?

Later on, when I foolishly grew up, I went to Canada and joined a rock 'n' roll band. Often, half-asleep in our bus, especially when travelling along the eastern coast the States, I would snap awake at the sound of what my subconscious mind recognised as a Northern-Ireland accent on the radio. Fully awake, I realised that it was that of an American newsreader. Odd, I thought. The two accents, half-heard out of context, are remarkably similar.

In between times, growing up as a Catholic in Stroke City, I was all too aware that things were not as they should have been. It was made clear to us that we were being barely tolerated in a Protestant state for Protestant people. We were Indians. Amongst the people with whom I grew up there was a resigned though reasonably cheerful recognition of the hopelessness of our position. Decent jobs were routinely denied us, as was decent housing and a democratic electoral system. Many of us didn't have a vote. Remember, this was still the case deep into the sixties.

Our hands were tied. At certain times during the year we were reminded of our lowly status by the various Orange parades which took over the main thoroughfares of Derry. These were triumphal, coat-trailing exercises. It wasn't the pipe or flute bands that were offensive. As a matter of fact, I used to enjoy listening to them, especially the bands that featured aggressive percussion. I was particularly fond of the Lambeg drum and still am today. The hair on the back of my neck still rises when I hear the distant thunder of the 'Fuck the Pope' bands.

No, the bands merely provided the soundtrack for the unruly and often less-than-sober camp-followers who, as is still the case today, were the main problem. It was sometimes hazardous merely listening to these bands. The musicians and marchers were often flanked by men who bore unsheathed swords, brandishing them theatrically in a bid to clear the way ahead for the bands and the knots of be-sashed men marching in between. I remember once straying a little too far from the kerb in order to get a better look at a particular drumming band when my short-trousered legs felt the brunt of the flatside of a flashing sabre. I can feel the cold steel yet.

I was physically hurt, embarrassed and felt deeply humiliated. So angered, in fact, that I made a decision never to watch the bands again. In future, whenever there was an Orange parade, I would go to the movies. The movies would be an escape for me, a refuge from the potential humiliation that waited outside.

And who better to cheer a young man up on a Saturday afternoon than the likes of John Wayne and Burt Lancaster, cowboys who regularly, three times a day, did what a man had to do, often in spite of great odds and often against the tide of public opinion?

Men who rode alone to escape a troubled past. The Lone Plains Drifters. And usually God-fearing men who had been brought up righteously, but who nevertheless lived their lives by their own rules. Men who would not deny that they were flawed individuals, constantly struggling with their demons.

Great stuff all round, and they also talked like my two old uncles in Donegal, yet another plus for me. How different these Lancasters and Waynes were compared to the marchers outside, whom I regarded then as thick, narrow-minded, intolerant, bigoted people whose idea of worshipping God did not seem at odds with treating nearly half the people in Northern Ireland like shite.

How deflated I was when, in the fullness of time. I discovered that Burt Lancaster's grandparents were from Belfast and that John Wayne was really one of the Morrisons from Randalstown, Co. Antrim. Protestant Ulster Scots to a man, John Wayne and Burt Lancaster were the same people as those who marched outside the cinema.

And my uncles' speech patterns were determined by the dialect of the Ulster Scots that my forebears had learnt when they were gradually weaned off their native Irish language.

My heroes were also the enemy.

I couldn't win.

I was running this over in my head as Ray whipped a bottle of Harp from the depths of his gigger's bag. He tore the metal cap off with his teeth and smiled evilly to himself as he put the beer to his lips. Yes, I could see him in the Alamo, telling the Mexicans to fuck off out of it. The Ulster Scots were good scalpers too and notoriously callous when it came to sorting out the Indians.

I think Ray would quite enjoy scalping people. Harpo too. Billy would be content to sketch them doing it.

The Ulster Scots are a proud people, proud of their heritage and proud of Northern Ireland, so proud of Northern Ireland that they made a complete bollocks of running the country and alienated half the population in the process, John Wayne or no fucking John Wayne.

———

But none of this concerned us greatly today, intent as we were on getting in and out of Belfast as quickly as possible.

We duly negotiated the border with its yawning Garda Síochána on the one side and the puzzled, drawn faces of eighteen-year-old squaddies

from Birmingham on the other. We found our way through Newry and
headed for Belfast.

Ray had finished off his beer and opened one of the large windows.
Leaning dangerously out of the speeding van on the port side, he
hurled the bottle at a roadside traffic sign that advertised a hump-
backed bridge ahead. The bottle somersaulted in the air and disintegrated on impact, scattering shards of glass in all directions.

This act of casual violence startled Harpo.

'You'll have somebody's eye out some day doing that!'

Ray had settled back in his seat by then.

He put his feet up against the back of the seat in front, chuckled to
himself, closed his eyes and settled in for a doze.

Belfast was changing. In 1972, because of the unfolding Troubles, the
city was slipping into a hibernation that was to last for more than thirty
years. Four short years earlier, things had been different. I was still with
The Chessmen at the time. We played in Belfast often and looked forward to playing in ballrooms like the Astor, the Orchid, Romano's, The
Plaza (where the general rule seemed to prevail that people couldn't
enjoy themselves on a night out unless they were sick a couple of times)
and, my favourite, the Floral Hall, picturesquely perched on a hill
beside Belfast Zoo. The Floral Hall was the only ballroom I knew where
a man could step outside for a smoke and hear the roar of several lions.

There were nightclubs too, more than in the larger city of Dublin,
where a man of even limited means could have a bite to eat, a drink or
two, witness a bit of so-so cabaret and round off the night with a not-
too-taxing jive with the lady of his choice. Pre-1969 Belfast was a good
place to be if you were a young buck on the loose in the city centre at
night. It wasn't to last long.

A case in point was the night in 1966 when The Chessmen were due to
play a routine Saturday-night gig in the Queen's Court Hotel in Bangor,
Co. Down. The Queen's Court was unique in that the gig was over at
ten o'clock due to a somewhat arcane adherence to the law as laid down
by Jesus via the Lord's Day Observance Society. This proved fortuitous
as, later on that night, the British group Cream were playing in Queen's
University in Belfast, Two Queens of a different nature. This was a rare

occasion to hear what was then reckoned to be the best rock group in the world, and the first so-called 'supergroup'.

Word circulated in Dublin that a relatively empty coach was travelling northwards. Consequently, we set off for Belfast in a van packed to the hilt with misfits.

We dropped our passengers off at the Uni and played the gig, returning later in time to hear Cream.

At one stage during their set, some of the Dublin contingent had gathered near the front of the stage. I remember thinking that this gig was special. On stage were Ginger Baker, Steve Bruce and Eric Clapton. Standing watching them was Phil Lynott (not yet part of Thin Lizzy), Rory Gallagher (already Rory Gallagher) and Henry McCullough (soon to be ex-Joe Cocker and ex-Paul McCartney's Wings).

Then the *coup de grace*. A small drunken member of the audience appeared beside us with a bottle of wine peeping from the pocket of his scruffy jacket. He swayed as he watched the band before presently turning to our drummer, gruffly demanding a cigarette. Our drummer complied and additionally provided the man with a light. This short inebriated person eventually lurched off toward the toilets.

'Uncommonly civil of you there, Terry' I remarked to my band mate.

He looked at me strangely.

'Don't you know who that was?'

'No.'

'Van Morrison.'

Little did we know the gems that lurked in the little man's temporarily befuddled head.

But that Belfast was receding into the past. What had been bubbling underneath was reaching the streets. The weasels were gnawing at the door.

Back to 1972, and we were stuck in rush-hour in that same city centre. I peered from the window and stared at the pedestrians scuttling swiftly by.

Belfast has always been a working-class town. These are no-nonsense people. I decided that many of the women I saw from the window were shorter than they ought to be and coping daily with perilously low centres of gravity. Too many had legs that were altogether too thick for office work; stout limbs developed by their great-grannies and grand-fathers through centuries of digging turf, pulling flax, picking spuds, pounding the roads, humping great swatches of hemp through the ropeworks, heaving sledgehammers, building *Titanics*—redundant legs, going to waste concealed behind desks.

Many of the men were short and generally stocky too, nervily weaving through the rush-hour throng, often wearing the type of jaunty little hat that used to be common on the heads of Italian organ-grinder's monkeys in films set on the streets of turn-of-the-century New York.

I noticed the characteristic urban walk adopted by both sexes: a labour-intensive walk, swift, short, bustling steps that seldom trans-ported the owner to his or her destination any quicker that if he or she had taken his or her time about it. My father used to walk like that. An urgent, fussy gait. Never did do him much good as far as I could gauge.

Just like any other city, I suppose. Except that this was not just another city. This was Belfast and it was five o'clock on a Friday after-noon—the start of the weekend in any white man's culture.

And in any other metropolis the heart of the city would naturally be preparing for the action at night: restaurants preening, pubs polishing, nightclubs gearing up and dance halls sweeping. Not here. This city centre would be practically deserted tonight. The pubs struggled game-ly on, opening staggered hours and waiting for better days, but only the foolhardy would drink here after dark. The bulk of customers failed to show up because they'd rather not run the risk of being blown through the ceiling before they'd finished their pint. Nor did they much look for-ward to being gunned down by a 'freedom-fighter' wearing a balaclava knitted by his mother.

Bad things happened that year. On the night of 11 July a number of drunken men broke into a family's home, killing a mentally handi-capped youth and raping his mother. This is the kind of thing we associate with the Siege of Stalingrad or the Fall of Berlin. But no, this was Belfast and acts like these were dismissed in some extreme quarters as sectarian high spirits.

Bloody Friday had occurred; twenty bombs exploded in the city centre in the space of an hour killing nine and cutting down 130 others.

People were staying at home. I would've done the same.

Some of the dance halls remained open and struggled on against the odds, but they would soon darken as those odds shortened.

Billy had remained silent during the course of the entire journey. He now became animated and was directing Harpo through busy thoroughfares until we finally turned off the main drag and came to rest down a side street.

Billy jumped out of the coach, cigarette jammed in mouth.

'Wait there,' he instructed Harpo. He jumped out and entered the doorway of what appeared to be some kind of auction house or art gallery.

'What's he going in there for?' enquired Lashback idly.

'The selfish bastard,' said Ray. 'He's dragged us all the way round here to pick up some fucking painting or other.'

It seemed that Ray was right. Billy reappeared toting something largish and rectangular, swathed in bubble-wrap.

'Fuck me,' sighed Harpo, under his breath, shaking his curly head.

It seemed that Billy had indeed lengthened our journey by decreeing that we travel to Donegal via Belfast for the purpose of furnishing his art collection. We would normally have taken the traditional and shorter route through Ardee, Castleblayney, Aughnacloy, Derry etc.

It was all the same to me. One set of potholes was much like another and, besides, what pressing alternative business did any of us have that day?

Billy sat with the package on his lap.

I wanted to ask him what it was and if I could have a look at it. I decided not to. I knew he would be feeling guilty about his selfishness but, being endemically selfish, couldn't help himself. I understood that.

One or two of the others weren't best pleased at being unnecessarily detoured in this manner. They wouldn't say anything or object, of course. Not to old Bill. They respected him too much. That's what he was like. Impossible to dislike.

I decided to ask him about the package later.

We were soon outside Belfast and speedily on our way to Derry. We were verging on lateness.

———

We left the M2 behind us (another motorway that predictably petered out when it reached areas infested with inferior beings) and found ourselves climbing slowly up the mountain that separated us from the long-expired town of Dungiven. We decided to stop the van for what Americans have taught us to refer to as a 'comfort break.'

As we pissed carelessly against the side of the van, ignoring the tootling horns of passing traffic, I looked back down the mountainside. We were almost at the highest point of the Glenshane Pass. A weak sun cast thin shadows over the bare beautiful hills. Sheep lazed and grazed by the side of the road. Mountain streams gurgled busily over the lichened rocks. Stretched below was the long glittering shape of Lough Neagh, surrounded on all sides by the serene flatlands of deceptively peaceful Ulster counties. Puffy clouds seemed only feet above us. A rainbow arched over the shining expanse of water below in the distance. We were literally over the rainbow.

Pat stood beside me, shaking his member a little too vigorously on the wrong side of decency for my liking.

'That's some sight,' he whispered. 'This could be God's seat.'

'Certainly could,' I replied, moving swiftly away.

We climbed back into the van.

Harpo revved the bugger up and we were off.

Pat sat opposite me. 'You know,' he said, gesturing at the landscape spread out below, when I see a sight like that its makes me wonder what you're all fighting about up here.'

'Hold on,' I said. 'Don't include me in that. I'm not fighting about anything.'

Pat didn't seem to hear. He continued. 'A United Ireland isn't worth the loss of one life,' he said.

I laughed heartily. He seemed upset at my sudden display of mirth.

'Did I say something funny?'

'I thought so, yes.'

'It's a serious business, dying for a country.'

'It's not about that. Nobody up here gives a fuck about a United Ireland,' I said.

Pat pursed his lips. Seemed upset. He paused for a minute or so. I waited him out.

'So, what's this fighting all about then?' he said.

Poor Pat.

'Do you want me to explain it to you?'

'Please do.'

'Oh, fuck!' grunted Ray. 'Here we go!'

'Let the man speak,' shouted Lashback.

It seemed I had an audience.

'Well,' I began. 'You'll normally see some arsehole from Belfast or Derry on television saying that he's fighting for a United Ireland and the world believes him. Even you people believe it. You who should know better but don't. What the arsehole doesn't tell you is that he's fighting because he's been treated like shite all his life by people who believe they're superior to him in every way. He doesn't tell you that because he's afraid they might be right.'

Ray shifted uneasily in his seat. He rubbed his eyes with his knuckles and pretended to look out the window.

'Who believes they're superior? The British Army?'

'No.'

'But aren't they his enemy?'

'No.'

'But isn't that who he's fighting?'

'Yes.'

'Then why is he fighting the British Army if they're not the enemy?'

'Because they're on the streets and he can see them.'

'So, why are the British here.'

'To prevent the arsehole from being killed.'

'Killed by who?'

'Killed by the enemy.'

'So, who's the enemy?'

'People who don't like him and think he's inferior.'

'Can we start this again,' said Pat.

'Not a bad idea,' chirped Eddie, joining in.

'He's talking through his hole,' interjected Ray.

Pat wasn't for giving up. 'So what about the Unionists or Loyalists or whatever it is you call them.'

'What about them?'

'Who or what are they loyal to?'

'The State.'

'You mean Great Britain?'

'Yeah.'

'What kind of people are they?'

'Decent people mostly, who've been lied to by those who run them. I suppose you could categorise them as displaced people if you're being fussy. Mostly of distant Scottish ancestry. They don't consider themselves Irish, but obviously aren't Scottish either. English people regard them as Paddies just like us. That drives them crazy. They're loyal to the British Crown and feel duty-bound to obey the laws of Britain when it suits them.'

I sneaked a look at Ray. He was pretending to be asleep.

'And what do they do if the laws don't suit them?'

'They bring the country to a standstill and beat British squaddies over the head with flagpoles flying the Union Jack.'

'What do the squaddies make of that?'

'It confuses them.'

'So, Loyalists are prepared to undermine the State and overturn the laws of the land?'

'Yes.'

'Why would they want to do that if they're loyal to the State?'

'To protect the State.'

'You say that Loyalists will fight the British Army too?'

'Only when the British Army doesn't do what Loyalists want it to do.'

'Which is what?'

'Wipe out people who are disloyal to the British State.'

Pat seemed confused. He screwed up his face in puzzlement.

'Let me get this straight, he said, slowly. 'Loyalists are disloyal to the British Crown because the British Army won't exterminate people who are disloyal to the British Crown?'

'Precisely.'

'Like Northern Republicans?'

'They have no real quarrel with the British Crown. It's a good life on the dole if you're not too ambitious and don't weaken.'

Ray was awake now. Probably couldn't stand it any longer. 'The fuckin' Nationalists do have a quarrel with Britain!' he cried.

'No they don't. They might've had in 1916. Now they're just angry because they've been treated like shite all their lives by their own countrymen.'

'By who?'

'By people in Northern Ireland who think they're inferior.'

'And are they?'

'Are they what?'

'Are they inferior?'

'No.'

'Are there many people in Northern Ireland who think these people are inferior?'

'Plenty.'

'That sounds dangerous.'

'It is. That's why the Army's here.'

'So, again. Who's the enemy?'

'People who think other people are inferior.'

Pat seemed to give up. 'None of this makes any sense to me,' he muttered.

'It's not supposed to,' I replied.

'Then how is the wider world supposed to understand what's going on up here?'

'People up here don't want the wider world to understand.'

'Why not.'

'Because then the wider world might make sensible suggestions about how to sort it out.'

'Wouldn't that be a good thing?'

'No.'

'Why not?'

'Because if people understood us and sorted out our problems we'd have no reason to live.'

'That bad, eh!' whistled Pat.

'Certainly is. Welcome to Northern Ireland.'

The sound of a raspberry came from directly behind.

'We should have left you guys behind when you were outside having a piss. At least you'd have been doing something constructive,' shouted Pat.

'Fuck off,' said three of us.

In unison.

14

The twin spires of Derry loomed into view, or rather, three, if one looked hard enough. We crossed the rickety old Craigavon Bridge and took a right turn which took us down a dusty street lined with grey three-storied commercial buildings that hugged the docks. The smell of the river hung in the air—an odour of times gone by. I fancied that if I opened a window I'd get to savour a whiff of dirty water leavened by the tang of foreign fags. I kept a weather eye out for infected Spanish sailors but they seemed thin on the ground.

I could see the river itself now, flat, languid and beautiful, like a tired old enemy. On the quayside were great piles of scrap iron and richly scented pine logs waiting to be loaded onto dirt-encrusted boats manned by shifty foreign merchant seamen, many of whom would be wearing small, dark moustaches. The strange thing about the River Foyle was that, although it was the most inviting of waterways, we locals never thought of using it for recreational purposes, nor did we take much notice of it as a functioning body of water, except as a means of supporting or buoying up the NATO ships from which we could extort small amounts of money. It was as if the river didn't belong to us. One would imagine that such an amenity elsewhere in the world would be used to the full, especially during summer, when people could sail, water-ski, row, swim, or do whatever it is that people do when blessed by sun and a crocodile-free expanse of shimmering water. But, no. It didn't happen in Derry. I had been on the river but once, aboard the steamer *Laird's Loch* on a daylight sailing to Glasgow with my mother on a trip to see my many Scottish aunts and cousins scattered across that even meaner city.

The Foyle wasn't part of our lives. I'm not sure why we didn't regard it as our river. Maybe we thought it belonged to somebody else.

But I did sometimes watch the older lads fish for eels and flounder from atop the wooden wharves. It was a grisly business. Lines and sinkers flew through the air, and whenever an unfortunate eel or 'flook' was hauled from the dark water, it was mercilessly hurled against the walls of the adjacent dockside storage sheds with great glee until it expired. I still remember the bloodthirsty whoops of the older boys as the desperately writhing eels and the flapping flounder sailed to their deaths.

I have never taken to fishing or to fishermen since.

I loved the bustle of the quays and patrolled them constantly during my pre-teenage years. I particularly liked to watch the flour and soya-bean meal boats unload. The loose cargo was sucked out of the ship's hold by a long mechanism resembling a giant straw. For mendacious reasons that I understood later, this operation required the constant presence of twenty-one dockers, all of whom stood urgently by watching the cargo being sucked up. After a certain time, they became completely coated by the thick white dust that wafted from the cargo, their motionless figures resembling featureless biblical pillars of salt.

It was getting late now, nearly six-thirty, but gruff flat-capped men with congealed shite on their boots and cigarettes dangling from their lower lips were still active, men who casually applied long sticks to the flanks of hapless cattle reluctant to board the Glasgow boat. Humans travelled on it too. I was totally in sympathy with the livestock. I had played a few gigs in Glasgow. I wouldn't have wanted to go there either.

Stand your ground, Cattle of Ireland! Your instincts are sound.

Further down the river, seawards, a Royal Navy destroyer squatted contentedly in its berth. She may yet have warlike deeds to perform if the deal ever went down and the natives rose properly as a body. There'd be no hiding place in the Bogside if that baby decided to swing her big guns to starboard.

We passed through a narrow stone arch that was part of Derry's walls. Remarkably well-preserved sixteenth- and seventeenth-century cannons poked from sturdy ramparts and pointed seawards. I often sat on the barrels of these great guns as a child, pretending to be repelling or, alternatively, rooting for the Spanish Armada. It was a precarious perch but no-one seemed to mind or discourage me. The drop was steep but no child had even been known to tumble. Probably because we weren't warned of the danger.

'How old are those walls?' asked Lashback.

'Early seventeeth-century I do believe,' I replied.

'Why were they built?'

'To keep the likes of you out.'

'Aw, don't start that again for fuck's sake,' screamed Pat, holding his face in his hands.

'It's amazing how they survived. How come they're still here?' continued Lashback.

'To remind you that they were built to keep the likes of you out.'

'Out of where?'

'Out of inside.'

'Inside of what?'

'Inside the walls where you had no right to be.'

'He's talking in riddles again,' said Ray disgustedly.

And Ray was right.

Except that he understood...

———

Derry was on the way down. It had woken up too late. The damage was irreparable.

As always, I felt little emotion as we drove through familiar streets. I didn't feel particularly excited about being back in my native city. I had been home for the weekend just a month before. It had been a surreal trip.

There had been sporadic rioting the night before and a chip shop had been razed to the ground. As I stood where the chip shop used to be, the smell of melted plastic hung in the air, wisps of smoke still rose from smouldering timber and the charred femurs belonging to a number of chickens reached upwards at skewed angles towards the sky. Coca-Cola concentrate oozed slowly from some Stygian underground soft-drink bunker, hissing and bubbling in the hot ash. Another significant blow for Ireland had been struck.

Only in Ireland can the downfall of the State be furthered by burning down a chipper belonging to a decent Protestant man.

A shambling figure appeared by my side. He was short, untidy and hunched. His soiled glasses were too big for his face, unruly hair flopping about his forehead in the stiff breeze.

The eyes glinted with the bright light of something akin to madness.

'Beat it up them,' he exclaimed softly, under his breath.

'Beat it up whom?' I was tempted to say but didn't, on two counts: (1) I sensed it unwise to seek clarification, and (2), people don't say 'whom' here.

I knew this man. A name came to me. It was 'Scatter'. I hadn't seen him in years. I'd forgotten his given name. But that was the name he answered to now. He had earned his unusual sobriquet during the course of a routine riot in the days (pre-1972) when ordinary respectable citizens would fling themselves recklessly at lines of armed British soldiers, secure in the knowledge that it was reasonably safe so to do. In much in the same manner as American students protesting about the Vietnam war felt free to push flowers into the extended barrels of Army rapid-fire rifles; the risk of being fired upon in earnest was regarded as less than minimal. This was before those ordinary respectable citizens realised what an army actually was; namely, a substantial body of men who are trained to shoot at whatever they're ordered to shoot at by the officer in charge at the time. Sentimentality rarely enters the frame.

Anyway, during the course of this recreational assault upon the troops, a sharp and sudden cry was heard from the rear of the throng. Heads turned to find one of their own wielding what appeared to be a functioning machine-gun. This was cause for general and genuine concern on two counts: Firstly, none of those participating in the riot had ever seen a machine-gun wielded in anger before, and secondly, if they really had to see a rapid-fire assault weapon this close, this was not the man they wished to see brandishing it, especially if they were situated, as they most surely were, directly in the line of fire.

Our man, unfazed, duly raised the weapon, pointed it at the troops and screamed, 'SCATTER!'

As people desperately spread-eagled on the ground, the gun went off, bucking and leaping in the arms of a man who had obviously received not even rudimentary training in handling rapid-fire weaponry. Bullets flew in every direction bar the one intended. In a nightmare of shameless havoc, shells ricocheted from the tops of tall buildings, smashed through distant windows and, according to some reports, clipped the tail of a protester's dog.

Our hero, aghast at his own recklessness and incompetence, stared at the smoking barrel in disbelief and managed to scuttle down an adjacent alleyway before the squaddies gathered themselves. He was lucky to have escaped with his life. The element of surprise had had the opposite effect. It had saved him. There was a silence as the solders stood slack-jawed and immobile. They weren't used to being attacked by lone, crazed gunmen who couldn't shoot straight. They would soon learn...

The people picked themselves up, embarrassed, and dusted themselves off; the mob magically melting away in shame, collectively muttering about the lunacy of the person who had given this man a gun.

And here stood 'Scatter' in the flesh.

'Haven't seen you for a while,' I said warily.

'Been away,' he grunted.

'Anywhere interesting?' I enquired.

'Hollywood,' he replied.

'*The* Hollywood?' After all, there was a Holywood in Co. Down.

'Yeah,' he sniffed. 'L.A.'

He fished a time-darkened dog-end from the depths of his donkey jacket.

I tried to picture him strolling down Ocean Boulevard in Santa Monica. The image didn't come.

'What were you doing there?' I asked.

'Working as a stuntman in the movies.'

I checked out the unlikely scrawny, spindle-shanked frame and sickly pallor.

'Hell of a job that. Risks involved.' I glanced around anxiously, seeking an escape route or another friendly face.

'Had to pack it in,' he offered.

'How come?'

He suddenly jutted out his jaw and thrust his bottom lip aggressively towards me until it was within an inch of my face. For a horrible moment I thought he was trying to kiss me. But no.

An erratic finger flew to the wizened mouth and pointed at a small blemish on the protruding lip.

'Cut my lip and had to come home.'

He wheeled violently and walked away.

So these were the guys who were being given automatic weapons. The future was secure. Ireland was in good shape. Scatter was on the case.

There was a time when nearly everybody had a nickname. A nickname could be either inherited or earned. Scatter's was of the latter variety. In a city where there were many dockers named 'Nash' or 'Doherty', individual members of 'clans' were given nicknames to differentiate them from other family members, but there were also nicknames that would commemorate glorious past deeds, recall embarrassing episodes, draw attention to behavioural tics, highlight physical deformity, reflect idiosyncrasies of some kind, including peculiar speech patterns, odd gaits and just about anything else that made a person stand out from the crowd. Inherited nicknames were somehow more respectful, reflected more gravitas and seldom insulted or diminished the bearer.

But the granting of nicknames was not confined to the stevedoring classes. It was part of the last traces of an Irish oral tradition, lingering from ancestral days in Donegal, a tradition that the Troubles would inevitably see off. Living on the fringe of the Bogside and spending much of my childhood there, I was surrounded by people who either had nicknames or used them always when referring to others. It was positively Runyonesque. A boy had to be mentally agile to keep up.

'Willy the Whang' would never be mistaken for 'Da Willy' or 'Willy One-Sock'. Who, ten years from now, will remember the brothers 'Banty', 'Toddler' and 'Slusher' Gallagher? What did cruel fate have in store for 'Nyiff-Nyaff', 'Joe Time Enough', 'Tuppenny Dan', 'Johnny the Pot', 'Barum Belly', 'Sour Guts', 'Scroofentail McDermott' (my favourite), 'Charlie Duck-egg' and 'Mickey No Arse'?

How will we address the descendants of 'Biscuit Hips', 'Fart McDaid', 'Ankles McGonagle', 'Spoon McShane', 'Biddy the Bee', 'John the Narrowman', 'Chinese Ornament', 'Fat Neck' and 'Fazook'?

Sometimes there was a rare confusion concerning identity. A popular street rhyme referring to a couple, the male of which enjoyed a puzzling pedigree, went as follows: 'Further down the street lived Maggie Jane and Ned McGurk. His name it was McDaid but he was McGurk at work.'

What World-War-II German bomb would have been capable of putting the wind up the likes of tough men like 'Blood Doherty', 'Chesty Crossan', 'Paddy the Hard', 'Packets McGilloway', 'The Daddler', 'Warpie', 'Ducksie' or 'Titsie'.

And stand up the man known as, simply, 'the Sock'.

One nickname was so graphic that females deemed it unutterable. This man was referred to in feminine circles as 'Hughie Bad Word'. The boys standing on the street corners knew him as 'Hughie Fuck'. In what acceptable manner could 'Hughie Fuck' possibly introduce himself to 'Limavady Liz'?

There was a family in the Bogside of the late fifties and early sixties who specialised in the production of male lead singers for showbands; specifically, three fine boys whose nicknames were 'Yockums', 'Spasms' and 'Gackums' (McGonagle), sired out of 'Wingy' McGonagle (so-called because he had lost his left arm in the War) not to be confused with the earlier-mentioned 'Ankles' McGonagle, of a different genus entirely. I often wondered if Wingy ever met an uncle of mine who had also lost an arm (the right one this time) in the same war. His name was Ambrose. People called him 'Amby' for short. Innocently enough, though, as very few people knew of the meaning or, indeed, the existence of the word 'ambidextrous.'

These nicknames were, of course, unsuitable for stage work. The McGonagle Three, so to speak, became, respectively, Martin Manners, Johnny Rivers and Jim Fontaine.

I played with Spasms in one of first bands I was in. The Gay McIntyre Showband ('Gay' being the bandleader's actual name) was the band I played with in Shorrocks Irish club in Manchester. And whilst we are on the subject, owned by a demolition contractor who gave us an occasional day's work which, naturally enough, often involved the random tearing down of houses. Neither I nor Spasms was very good at demolishing houses. One day an oxy-acetylene bottle fell on his leg, breaking it badly. We packed in the gig and went home to Derry whilst he remained in hospital with his shattered limb suspended in a sling. He wasn't best pleased at being deserted. He never came home again, marrying a small, blonde Polish girl who looked after him after we'd left him to his fate. He understood. We weren't all that sentimental.

Until last year, I hadn't seen any of the McGonagle brothers for twenty years. However, one night, home in Derry and enjoying a quiet drink in a local bar, an older man sidled over to me and whispered starkly, 'Rivers has gone.'

There were no pleasantries, no introductory hellos, no hesitant reminder or explanatory preamble of any kind. No, none of that. Just a bald, 'Rivers has gone.'

It was Martin Manners breaking the news that Johnny Rivers had passed on.

The Trinity had been disrupted.

But, then again, that's what Derry was like. A native is never allowed to feel that he is out of the loop. No matter how many years have elapsed. One is assumed to possess the facility of instant recall regarding every aspect of Derry life, even if one hasn't been home for twenty years—a forced inclusivity that often borders on the pathological.

———

'Is your house fixed up yet? Hope you aren't planning on dropping in to your Mum's for a fry,' shouted Harpo. 'We're touch and go, timewise.'

Took the words right out of my mouth.

'Carry on, sir,' I replied. 'Proceed directly to the gig. I'll be back here tomorrow.'

I wouldn't have minded calling in to say hello. Tomorrow would be time enough. Gerry Time Enough. Anyway, the house in which I was born, my home, had lost its magic for me when bombed by the IRA a year before and was very far from being 'fixed up.'

By all accounts, the bombing mission was a routine operation. We lived in a rented Victorian house on Sackville Steet, on the fringe of the Bogside. It was a three-storey house, large by any standards, with five functioning bedrooms. For reasons still not clear, we paid a peppercorn rent. Consequently, the landlord devoted his life to evicting us. He seemed to regard it as a challenge.

A grocery store occupied the ground floor. A 'freedom fighter' strolled in and placed a large bomb on the counter-top. The place was duly evacuated but nobody thought to inform my mother who was home alone upstairs, busily applying Brasso to her door knobs on the third-floor bedrooms. The bomb duly exploded, ripping great holes in the ceilings.

She emerged dusty and unhurt. A miracle.

I rushed home when told the news. When I walked up the street, I saw my father searching for his pipe in a pile of rubble.

The house looked sound enough from the outside but the interior was a mess. My bedroom looked as if it had been swatted by a giant fist. A heavy bronze Nazi eagle that my father had liberated from a surrendered German U-boat was embedded in the ceiling. It usually sat on top of the upright piano in our front room. The piano was now a heap of splintered wood. But the house didn't fall down. It just kind of skewed to the left, like one of those rickety, crooked houses we see illustrated in Grimm's fairy tales.

'Are your folks still living there?' enquired Harpo.

'Yeah,' I said.

'Why?'

'Cos they don't want to leave. Some of the floors are buckled to an angle of fifteen degrees.'

'That's dangerous.'

'Only if you're not careful where you tread.'

'How can they live like that?'

'They love the house. It's their home.'

'Fucking I.R.A.'

'They apologised, you know. For blowing the house up.'

'Bastards.'

And they did. A mild-mannered, albeit inarticulate young man came to call at our family ruin, offering apologies on the grounds that the 'lads' had thought the premises above the shop unoccupied.

There's ace intelligence-gathering for you, I thought. There were a number of obvious clues that could lead to the conclusion that the premises were occupied. Let's see, how about the regular phenomenon of lights blazing in most of the rooms every night, a family car permanently parked outside the front door, people going in and out of the house all day, prams belonging to visiting grandchildren parked daily outside the front door?

No Sherlock-Holmes intuition or forensic expertise required there.

The country was safe in the hands of these men.

'How'd they make a mistake like that?' asked Harpo.

'Because they know little and care less.'

'What does that mean?'

'I don't know myself.'

I tried not to think about it.

Even though I wasn't living at home, I felt that part of me was gone. In truth, I suppose I felt homeless.

——

Winding through the centre of Derry now, across Guildhall Square, near my family home, my eyes rose to gaze fondly at the four-faced clock of the Victorian Guildhall and remember that its northern clock face was the first thing I saw each morning when I woke in my attic room, stood on the end of the bed, prised the skylight window open, and gazed across the Peter-Pan rooftops at the world below as the great time piece chimed eight bells. Back then the world belonged to me in the morning.

I could hear the bells of the old clock sounding out now as we drove past, at exactly five o'clock, a familiar musical clang, the peal of which made me feel like a child again, getting ready to go to school. I felt briefly comforted.

Not for long though. My stomach knotted as we drove down the dreary Strand Road, past the street where my lop-sided home tottered on its last legs. I could barely bring myself to throw it a cursory glance as we inched past the south end of Sackville Street, the street where I was born.

However, I was glad I managed to sneak a peek. I had momentarily forgotten about the girls. The street was teeming with them, with more pouring through the main gate of Hogg and Mitchell's shirt factory, a huge, squat, red-brick Victorian edifice that ran almost the entire length of the street opposite our house. Their work day over, the girls cheerfully swung home, often arm in arm with one or two of their workmates. Nothing untoward or Sapphic, just a closeness that developed between women who worked side by side on the various shop floors, involved in the complicated process of making shirts for export.

I had grown up with these girls, these cuffers, smoothers (they ironed the shirts), banders, front-stitchers, back-stitchers, sleevers, button-holers and those who specialised in the creation of collars. Fifteen hundred girls, aged from eighteen to sixty worked in the factory. There were one or two men about, mechanics who fixed the various machines and maintained other mysterious contraptions, men who generally lived in fear at the ever-present prospect of being cheerfully debagged and deposited in the street by a flock of laughing women.

And these were strong, independent, attractive women. I was fascinated by their broad smiles and uniformly good teeth. I judge that my childhood memory is accurate when I see old photographs of groups of women who were young back then: big smiles, flashing teeth, a tubby person a rarity. When I was growing up, none of these girls or women ever seemed down, depressed or even a hair less than jolly.

I loved the joy of life that radiated from them. And, of course, their lives were tough enough outside the factory gates, too, but somehow I never saw signs of it in their demeanour. I was aware of the cramped conditions which most of the workers had to endure at home, often two large families jammed into a crumbling, small-scale two-up, two-down. I was lucky. Our house was big by any standards.

And we had factory girls staying with us, five or six usually at any given time, girls from the surrounding countryside who maintained that the difficulties of commuting between the city and their bucolic homes on a daily basis were insurmountable. Lodgers, as it were.

The fact that the city dance halls were jumping every night in no way influenced their decisions. My mother provided bed and board for a pittance—boarders was another term. I regarded them almost as sisters, although I did have a perfectly good and real sister of my own.

We also housed two bus drivers, Fred and Ernie, on a permanent basis. These were two taciturn single men in their thirties who had slicked back hair and smoked heavily. I always thought of them as the kind of men who were the first to be killed in wars. There was a solidness and fundamental decency about them that was almost visible. They habitually wore long, belted, heavy, double-breasted overcoats be it summer or winter, the kind of overcoats with big, roomy pockets that jingled with loose change. A penny or two, a rogue bar of chocolate or a handful of sweets were often produced from these glorious repositories and placed in my extended hand with a friendly grin.

We also entertained a permanent resident by the name of Rose. She was getting on a bit, perhaps all of fifty years old, what was known then as a spinster, and not a little eccentric. She wore a dun-coloured coat and a little tan beret. Rose's lips were permanently pursed and her face pinched. She was friendly in her own way, though, and seemed to suffer from a pathological fear of germs. She bought and prepared her own food, the remains of which were hermetically sealed and stored in little brown paper sachets.

Rose occupied a small attic room into which no-one was allowed to stray. I sneaked into it often when everyone was out. It had a peculiar smell, something akin to embalming fluid. Layers of old newspapers were draped over every elevated surface, including the bed. Only the linoleum-covered floor was allowed to see the light that God sent in through the skylight window. I enjoyed the heady, antiseptic aura of eccentricity.

On the third floor of our house we had a self-contained apartment, something that was regarded at the time as the oddest thing. It was a cavernous front-facing room with a gas cooker in one corner, a shrine to the Blessed Virgin in the other, a three-barred gas fire, a sturdy table, two chairs and a large bed so elevated I could hardly climb into it. I wasn't allowed to enter this room but, of course, couldn't resist it if afforded half a chance.

In this bed-sit lived, periodically, a Petty Officer of the British Navy, a silent, precise man who made little sound of any kind when in residence—the type of man whom people used to describe as 'compact'. My mother paid him the greatest compliment when she stated with wonder that 'you'd never know he was there at all.'

For reasons that I'm sure were operational and probably pedestrian, certain ships of the British Navy spent long periods in the port of Derry. One of the perks of being an officer was the freedom to live ashore whilst the vessel was in port. Our little Petty Officer cut a small but impressive figure in the crisp naval uniform he wore at all times. It was odd to get out of bed in the morning and meet a uniformed naval officer on the landing. He was polite, spoke to no-one other than a nod and a curt hello but was, on the whole, perfectly amenable.

So, let's see, under one roof there was my mother and father, me, two brothers and one sister, six factory girls, permanent Rose, two bus drivers and a non-commissioned officer of the British Navy who cooked for himself. Add to this, the constant comings and goings of my brother Johnny's musician friends and we have a nucleus of a fairly lively household. You can imagine that, under the circumstances, loneliness was never an option.

Mealtimes were particularly fraught. It may seem odd to some that I sometimes had to join a queue for lunch in my own home.

I loved every minute of it.

But the factory girls across the street were the big attraction. Their standard hours of work were from eight a.m. to five in the afternoon, with lunch (called 'dinner' then) from one p.m. until two and a ten-minute break at eleven a.m. and two p.m. (called, not unusually, the Ten Minutes) These ten-minute breaks were frantic affairs. Fifteen hundred women had just that amount of time to consume a sticky bun and then deal with a hurriedly lit single cigarette, all bought in the only convenient shop situated around the corner in Great James Street. That shop belonged to my uncle James (not, alas, *the* Great James). This was fortuitous as I usually made it my business to loiter in the shop at exactly eleven a.m. and again at two p.m. I found it quite pleasant to be squashed by hundreds of girls. 'Twas all quite innocent, of course. I kept to myself as much as was humanly possible. I just enjoyed being in their company and in close proximity. Let's say that these experiences were quite formative. Maybe they indicated a path I should follow.

Most of the girls were single but many were married with children. The majority of workers, single or hitched, lived in the Bogside, where the male unemployment rate was probably somewhere in the region of eighty per cent.

You might think that this would provide ample opportunities for a little healthy role reversal, but you'd be wrong. This was the mid- to late-fifties. Women did everything in the home. They prised the children from bed, got them dressed, fed and off to school, ferried breakfast to the resting silverbacks upstairs and then went to work. During the day, the men listened to the radio, walked greyhounds, played cards, con-gregated around lampposts and on street corners, shot the breeze, played shove ha'penny, backed horses, wrestled with each other, smoked dog-ends, and spat on the pavement.

These were alpha males striving gamely to keep their end up in a matriarchal society. They didn't have to try too hard. The extraordinary thing was that these women did not expect the men to help look after the children or to ease the burden of household chores. The women accepted the unassailable fact that men were men and weren't expected to cook and clean, even if they had nothing else to do. Sounds to me like an uncommonly healthy attitude.

I didn't much care for the men who gathered at the street corners. They were outwardly boorish and menacing. Of course, when they all got together I suspected that they lived in quiet dread of being ridiculed or negatively bantered by each other. When I was young, I never understood why my father would never speak to me if I encountered him in the street when he was with his mates. Even if I met him on the street when he was walking alone, a barely perceptible nod of the head would be the extent of his greeting. I still feel the same today about men in groups, and shudder when I think of golf club dinner dances—different income bracket, same macho defensive arseholes...

On summer days, I would often sit in our 'good' first-floor room, looking down across the street where I could see the girls working at their broad tables on the ground floor of the factory. I could see them through the upper panes of the windows, always kept open to let in a breath of air. I would open one of our big windows too, not to facilitate airflow this time, but to hear the girls sing along to an old BBC radio programme called 'Music While You Work', a fifteen-minute twice-daily medley of popular tunes, often played by a brass band. It was a wondrous sound. I can still hear 'She Wears Red Feathers and a Hula, Hula Skirt' (sounded like 'hooley' to me, not yet aware of what a Hula skirt might be), 'Shrimp Boats are A' Coming' and 'Open the Door, Richard'. I also remember 'That's Amore', which contained a line that baffled me. I now know the line to be, 'When the Moon hits your eye like a big pizza pie, that's amore.' We didn't know what a pizza was so, though a tad illogical, we happily sang, 'when the moon hits your eye like a big piece of pie, that's a more eh?' We didn't speak much Italian either.

I also noticed something that years have taught me to regard as unique about the women of Derry. When they sang along to the tunes they heard on 'Music While You Work,' they automatically slipped into three-part harmony. Elsewhere in the white man's world, groups of women (or men) who break into spontaneous song tend to sing the melody only. Only in African countries or in other areas populated by our darker brothers do people tend to sing three-part harmony during a knees-up.

This was my tribe and I loved them.

But the girls would soon be gone. The Troubles were talking hold and shirts were being made more cheaply elsewhere. The shirt factories would soon be silent.

The women would go home to stay. The men would barely notice.

We drove on.

Otherwise and elsewhere, there was the usual general aura of defeat about the city. It hung in the air like a wet blanket drooping from a clothes line. I felt the old familiar chill. The main thoroughfare had been recently bombed again and workmen were busy clearing the last jagged bits of glass, rubble and shredded woodwork from a gap in the street that, up until only a matter of a day or so ago, had been occupied by a distinguished old building housing a long-established family business.

Evidence of collateral damage was visible all around: stripped roofs and new panes of glass with white sticky tape still attached. No-one killed this time around. Some of the pedestrians now pushing prams past the debris mightn't be so lucky next time. In due course, a new but inferior building would arise after the archaeologists had been given the usual go-ahead to poke about. It's an ill wind. Archaeologists couldn't help but love the Troubles. People had been living in this general city area for fifteen hundred years. Buildings were being blown up in the city centre that had been standing undisturbed for three hundred years. What archaeologist wouldn't give every trowel he owned for a peek under the likes of those?

An archaeologist based in a local college once brought me to a warehouse piled to the roof with warped medieval wine bottles, ancient cracked chamber pots, gnarled human bones, clay pipes of all sizes, shards of bronze cooking pots, rusted cannonballs, unidentified slivers of metal, remnants of leather sandals, boots with no provision for laces and, the piece de resistance, a more-or-less complete medieval brick kiln—all culled from underneath suddenly removed premises.

People have been walking these winding streets for a very long time. Perhaps too long.

15

W e enjoyed a smooth ride until we reached the border town of Strabane, a settlement that was, if it were possible, even more downtrodden and neglected than Derry. The roads, of course, deteriorated immediately we crossed the border. As we bounced through Barnes Gap, great slopes of shale and jagged rock ascended steeply on each side of the road. Lashback had to be physically restrained from leaping from the coach and clambering up the rugged scree. He wanted to climb a mountain, he said. We had to explain to him that even the indigenous sheep were having difficulty remaining upright. He was hard to calm. Must've taken something extra that we didn't know about.

Our rendezvous point with O'Brien was a major and favoured hotel in Donegal Town, a place we knew well, a place where a man could replenish himself with a fine steak, home-made chocolate éclairs and regale others in front of an open fire with a hot whiskey in his mottled fist.

We piled out of the van, pushed our way through the usual small knot of urchins clambering over the vehicle, and walked into the foyer of the hotel. The old man sat in his wheelchair near an open turf fire.

All was well.

This man was known to us as the Keeper of the Antiques.

It was an old-fashioned hotel: tired red drapes, threadbare carpet and faded flock wallpaper. The foyer was festooned with Relics of Old Decency. It reminded me of my granny Anderson's house in Derry. Her Relic of Old Decency was tea with silver service every afternoon at four. One must keep up appearances even when one's circumstances have been reduced.

The foyer of the hotel was home to two free-standing brass urns, ancient firearms nailed to the walls, dusty paintings depicting long-forgotten fox-hunts, portraits of stern women with long noses, and a variety of other bric-à-brac of varying interest and antiquity.

The Keeper of the Antiques displayed the same long nose as the ladies in the portraits. The genes persist. He sat there daily, nursing small whiskeys in his pasty crippled hands. His demeanour was that of a discarded ventriloquist's dummy, with his staring eyes, perpendicular shock of dyed-black hair and immobile, undefined facial features. He looked not unlike the actor Micheál MacLiammóir, whom I regularly observed drinking and holding court in another hotel, Groom's in Dublin, opposite the Gate Theatre. Orson Welles once wrote that MacLiammóir looked like something that Aubrey Beardsley might have drawn if somebody had taken away his pencil sharpener. I understood exactly what he meant. Ditto the Keeper.

I paused by his side whilst the others lurched towards the hotel bar. He smelled slightly of piss and strongly of whiskey. Better than the other way around, I reflected.

'Good evening, sir,' I said. 'How's business?'

He seemed startled.

'Can't get the staff,' he snapped. 'Bloody Irish Government. Do I know you?'

'Yes, we've been here a number of times. Two months ago was the last time. Brown and O'Brien, you know? Band? From Dublin?'

'He's here now,' said the Keeper.

'Who?'

'O'Brien. Nice chap.'

'Where is he?'

'In my son's office.'

'Talking about golf, rugby and other people's money?'

'Pardon?'

'Never mind.'

I looked beyond the reception desk though the half-and-half frosted/plain glass of a private office and spotted the shaggy but neatly coiffed head of Mike O'Brien nodding in animated conversation with the manager of the hotel. I knocked on one of the panes and was waved in.

'Howya, head!' beamed O'Brien.

There was something about the office that felt nastily familiar. There was that same musty smell, same straight-back chairs with brass-pinned squares of leather on the seats, same old roll-top desk, yellowish wallpaper, loudly ticking stern clock on the wall, the same old-fashioned, upright, wooden telephone switchboard with tens of sockets for brown jack-plugs that dangled on frayed, grey wires, same squat Telex machine and, in a conspicuous corner, a Pitney-Bowes franking machine.

Jesus Christ, I muttered. All that was missing here was the thunder of dockers' boots on the stairs and the angry clamour of drunken short-changed men. I hadn't been in an office like that since. Until now. I snapped out of it.

Mike O'Brien sat puffing a revolting cigar and looked quite the dandy in his bum-freezer jacket and winklepicker shoes.

He was schmoozing the johnny. I knew not to interfere and took a seat as beckoned by the manager, a mousey looking man who looked like the Keeper must have done before whatever had happened to him had happened to him.

Mike was doing his Elvis routine. He only performed it deep in the country as it seldom played well in densely populated areas.

'I had a drink with him a number of times,' drawled Mike. 'Quiet, unassuming kind of chap. Didn't gargle a lot. Just the occasional glass of red wine. And, like most of us, enjoyed a good cigar.' O'Brien cackled and projected a puff of cigar smoke towards the ornate flowered lampshade that hovered a number of feet above his head.

The hotel manager was on the hook. O'Brien was an easy and competent liar. Nothing malicious. Just show-business talk and there was nothing wrong with that. I liked O'Brien and understood, as he did, that an important function in the role of any showband lead singer was to impress those who knew no better. And he had to do it double because of Billy Brown's lack of inclination to talk to anybody who might bore him. O'Brien was flying the flag for all of us, flying it for show business. We understood that. Can't have people believing that we're little better that the punters who pay in to see us. We move in different circles, don't we? We're stars, aren't we? Go get 'im, O'Brien.

'He's polite,' O'Brien continued. 'Calls everybody "sir" or "ma'am".'

'Get away,' exclaimed the manager, eyes as big as saucers shining in his head.

These were early days before the information revolution when the man in the street knew little. Pros like O'Brien professed to have the inside gen, true bill, the Knowledge.

O'Brien, needless to say, knew Elvis the same way the rest of us did, staring dully at the King's shite post-US-Army movies from the one-

and-nines in the local flea-pit, chain-smoking Woodbine cigarettes, nursing a bag of melting Maltesers, and reaching round the seat beside us trying to cop a feel of some virgin's leg.

I had never taken to Elvis anyway, holding firm to my conviction that the Army finished him. I was an in-betweenie anyway. Born in 1944, I was marginally too young to be smitten by Elvis and too old to hero-worship The Beatles. There was nothing left for me but a healthy cynicism. Later, in the seventies, when I ended up playing in a Canadian/American rock band, I learned more about Elvis from people who knew him well. None of what I heard was good.

The manager produced two glasses that were almost clean, reached into a cabinet that looked seldom troubled, hauled out a semi-decent bottle of whiskey and poured us a healthy glass each.

'By the way, this is Gerry,' expanded O'Brien. 'You know my colleague, Gerry. He plays bass guitar.'

I reached over and lightly took the manager's outstretched hand. I'm a bad hand-shaker. Always have been.

'Finbarr's the name,' announced Finbarr, swiftly disengaging from my limp paw.

Finbarr wasn't interested in me, all the while glancing at O'Brien.

'Do you keep in touch?' he said.

'Pardon?' said O'Brien, unwittingly flicking ash from the tip of his cigar onto the top of his wickedly-pointed shoe.

'With, you know, Elvis?'

'Now and again. I try not to bother him. El values his privacy.'

Ah, fucking El it was now. I felt I had to intervene before O'Brien invited Finbarr to Graceland for a fortnight's holiday, sorry, vacation.

'Drive down uneventful, was it?' I enquired, turning to O'Brien.

'Fair to middling,' he said, fashioning a smoke-ring with a pucker. 'Steering on the Merc feels a bit loose. Not handling well. Tends to pull to port. Can you get someone to look into that when we get home?'

'Will do,' I smiled. Three fucking bags full, sir.

It was part of the act. He was the Star. That's how things worked. Perception was all. The bigger a star he appeared in the eyes of others, the better we tended to fare.

I rose to leave.

'I'll just check on the others,' was my parting shot.

Crossing the hall, I nodded again at the still but alert figure of the Keeper and entered the hotel lounge bar.

The Woodentops were standing at the bar giggling and poking each other with scrawny elbows. I wasn't surprised to see them. Donegal Town was well within striking range of their home base in Sligo. I smiled thinly and waved. They waved back but didn't approach. They knew better than to impose. This was their only saving grace, a mark of the professional ride. They never joined the company until they were invited. At least they had a bit of cop-on.

The rest of the band sat around a table near the fire. They would get round to the Woodentops soon enough.

It was only a matter of time.

Our lads had gathered in the corner of the lounge. We more or less had the place to ourselves. I joined them and stared at the turf fire.

'Where's the gig, head?' enquired Ray, sucking steadily on an untipped cigarette whilst rhythmically stroking his beard as usual.

I was surprised by his curiosity. He normally didn't care where he went.

'It's not a fuckin' marquee, is it?' demanded Lashback anxiously. Drummers hated tents. The canvas killed the sound of the drums. Muffled and flattened the sound of everything else, too, but, then again, we didn't physically exert ourselves as much as his particular calling demanded. At least if nobody could hear my bass guitar, I didn't lose a gallon of sweat trying to make up for it. It was impossible for the likes of me to try harder, tied down as I was by the limits of electricity.

'No, it's a hall. Not too big as far as I'm told. And not too far from here. Bally-something,' interjected Harpo.

'That narrows it fucking down a lot,' snorted Eddie, sarcastically

'It wouldn't want to be too far away,' said Pat, unhappy in a corner. 'It's after seven o'clock.'

'Any talk of a meal for the boys?' I asked Harpo, who was supposed to be on top of these necessary details.

'Apparently we'll get something in the hall,' he replied, looking over his shoulder at three women in their early thirties who were fussing about in the act of occupying the table next to us. One of the women was wearing a particularly low-cut blouse. She made the mistake of removing her coat.

'A meal in the hall,' cried Lashback. 'No thanks. I've had all the ham salad I'll ever need. FUCK HAM SALAD!'

He was still a little high. I threw him a stern look. So did the ladies. The shouted words 'fuck ham salad' constituted a phrase that the three ladies were obviously unaccustomed to hearing in the lounge of a respectable hotel, especially when howled aloud by a long-haired misfit with staring eyes.

The one with the chest glared in our direction and addressed us. 'I'll thank you to mind your language,' she said, slowly but with some authority.

Lashback's reply was swift. 'And I'll thank you if you show us the rest of your tits.'

This was the wrong thing to say for a number of reasons. The twofold implication being (a) that she was showing a little too much tit already, and (b) that she may have had more than two tits. She evidently found this approach unacceptable. She stood up angrily and marched towards Lashback.

Suddenly Billy Brown appeared between them. He raised a conciliatory hand and placed in gently on the woman's arm. He looked into her eyes for a moment, just long enough for her to recognise him. It was good to be known. Her resistance evaporated. Dead meat, I think is the expression.

Billy adopted his best stutter, reserved, I always suspected, for times such as these.

'Forgive my f-f-f-friend, dear. J-j-j-just a little high s-s-s-spirits. Please ac-c-c-cept our apologies. W-w-w-won't happen ag-g-gain. Let me b-b-b-buy you and your f-f-f-riends a drink. C-c-c-ome with me.'

With that he led her gently to the bar. She was his forever. I wished I could do that.

The eyes of the other girls followed the new couple's progress to the bar with envy. The rest of us might as well not have been present.

That's why Billy was Billy and we weren't. It was a matter of charisma. It can't be developed. If it isn't there, forget it.

'That one with the tits looks like Mabel, doesn't she?' exclaimed Eddie.

'You think so?' I replied.

'Who's Mabel?' asked an unrepentant Lashback.

'Never you mind,' I said. 'If I was you I'd cool it for a while. What are you on anyway?'

He didn't answer.

'You can tell me,' chimed Pat. 'Who's Mabel?'

I smiled at Eddie.

Eddie smiled back

I smiled at Pat. 'I'll tell you some other time, perhaps.'

Pat didn't smile back.

'Maybe O'Brien'll tell us,' said Ray, as Mike appeared in the room, shaking Finbarr's hand in gratitude for the parting glass. They separated and Finbarr strode out the front door into the street, totally ignoring the Keeper of the Antiques.

Mike O'Brien approached us with a broad smile. 'Somebody had to spoof the Johnny!'

He spotted Billy seated with the women and swiftly and instinctively joined them with nary another word to us nor a backward glance.

He pulled up a chair beside the least ugly one that wasn't the one showing her tits, whom Billy had already claimed. He had her laughing before his bum had settled on the chair.

'Ah,' whispered Ray, 'the joy of observing professionals at work.'

It turned out that Billy had inadvertently struck gold. The three women were young marrieds from Belfast who were staying in the hotel as part of a get-to-know-you weekend away sponsored by the firm for which they worked. Their husbands were at home and their male colleagues had disappeared somewhere to play golf and drink.

The fools, the fools, they'd left us their married bored…

———

It was nearly eight o'clock before we piled back into the van. This was unconscionably late in any man's language but Harpo had assured us that all would be well if the band gear was set up by ten o'clock, by which time the relief band would be present and ready to play, allowing us to go to another pub again.

Harpo seemed to know where he was going so we didn't bother to ask, content that our ultimate destination lurked not too far away.

Eddie sat beside me rolling a joint.

'What've you got?' I enquired.

'Paki Black,' he replied, moistening the gummed end of his cigarette papers.

'That'll do nicely.' It was a little strong for this stage in the proceedings but what the fuck.

He took a few deep drags and passed it to me. I did likewise and ignored Lashback's loud demand for inclusivity.

The joint went back and forth between Eddie and me until it was gone. And so, shortly, were we.

We sat in silence, listening to the delicious whine of the engine and the annoying sound of Lashback humming desperately two rows behind and drumming his fingers on the armrest of his seat.

Eddie cocked his head.

'Do you think I'm taller than Dustin Hoffman?' he suddenly asked.

The query took me by surprise. Nevertheless, I knew why he was keen to know. Eddie was not the tallest of men and like, many short people, desired to be taller.

I could tell that his was going to be one of our special conversations. We had them every once in a while. It kept us sharp. The dope helped.

'How tall is he anyway?' said Eddie.

'How tall is who?'

'Dustin fucking Hoffman!'

'Less than five feet tall.'

'How much less?'

'He's four feet eleven inches tall.'

'Jaysus, that's really on the short side.'

'You don't get much shorter than that without being classed as a midget.'

'How short do you have to be before you can get your midget certificate?'

'Oh. I dunno. Slightly shorter than that.'

Eddie paused. He seemed confused.

'Shorter than what?' he said.

'Shorter than Dustin Hoffman. You're not listening.'

He remained unfazed and pursued a similar line of thought whilst engaged in the mechanics of rolling another joint.

'It's amazing the number of Hollywood stars who are shorter than you think they are,' he grunted, fumbling with the Rizlas.

'How do you know how short I think they are?'

'Figure of speech. I imagine you were surprised when you found out that Dustin Hoffman was only four foot eleven.'

'Little Big Man.'

'Yes, I suppose he is.'

'No. Dustin Hoffman starred in a film called "Little Big Man".'

'Did he?'

'Yes. Good movie. About an old Indian who wouldn't die. Dustin Hoffman was short even for an Indian.'

'Why was he so short?'

'There's no answer to that. It's like asking why there's a moon in the sky. Give us a puff o' that, will you?'

He handed me the completed new joint. I continued, airily waving the lumpy fag. 'It's like asking why people like Charlie Drake. There's no explanation for it. Dustin Hoffman's just short. That's the way of it. Charlie Drake's a tiddler too.'

'So how did he get into the movies being so short and all?'

'Charlie Drake?'

'No, Dustin fuckin' Hoffman.'

My head was swimming now. Excellent.

'Hollywood likes short people. Humphrey Bogart was only five feet four inches tall.'

'That's five inches taller than Hoffman. Compared to him, Bogart was a giant.'

'And Al Pacino's only five foot six.'

'What about Mickey Rooney? He's so small he's practically invisible.'

'Mickey Rooney's four inches taller than Dustin Hoffman.'

'Fuck off!'

'He is.'

'How do you know all this, anyway?'

'It's in a book at home.' I handed the joint back to him.

There was a bit in it yet.

'Ask me why most movie stars are short,' I said.

'I've already asked you. You said there was no answer to that.'

'That's because you asked me the wrong question.'

'Well, tell me the right question to ask and I'll ask it.'

'Ask me why so many short people do so well in the movies.'

'Do you know why so many short people do well in the movies?'

'Ask me and you'll find out.'

'I've just fucking asked you!'

'Did you?'

'Yes.'

'Short people do well in the movies precisely because they're short.'

There was a brief silence. Eddie rubbed his right eye with his knuckles and sighed. 'And that's it?' he said.

'More or less.'

'I'll ask you again. Why do short people do well in the movies because they're short?'

'Because their facial features are more symmetrical than taller peoples.'

'Bollocks.'

'Not bollocks at all. Short people photograph better than tall people. Their noses, eyes and cheekbones tend to be more delicate, refined and evenly spaced. All I'm saying is that their features tend to be arranged more neatly. Cameras like that.'

'And tall people don't look so good?'

'Sometimes they do. Sometimes they don't. Mostly they tend to look big and move clumsily. And their features tend to be cruder and all over the place, geometrically speaking.'

'Geometrically? So is that it?'

'No, there's more. Apart from having symmetrical faces, short people tend to possess more drive and ambition than taller people. They don't give up easy.'

'Why's that?'

'Because they're short. They feel inferior. Look at Napoleon and Jimmy Clitheroe.'

Eddie howled with laughter. It was the dope. 'The Clitheroe Kid!'

Jimmy Clitheroe was a diminutive half-man/half-boy British radio and television comedian. The term 'Clitheroe Kid' was, of course, widely used by heads when referring to a small but indispensable component of the female anatomy.

'I never thought those two had much in common,' he yelped.

'But you do see it now, don't you?'

'I don't know if I do or not.'

'And, of course, there is a downside to being a short movie star. Picture the scene. Your new movie is holding its premiere in Dublin. You've never been to Dublin before. You're driving down the quays past Liberty Hall towards the bus station in a stretch limousine. People line the streets.'

'Where am I going?'

'You're not going anywhere. It's Dustin Hoffman's limousine. He's in it. You're not in the car. He doesn't know you.'

'Ok. So where's Dustin Hoffman going?'

'I told you. He's going to the premiere of his new film.'

'Where's it at?'

'The Savoy.'

'Then why is he being driven down the quays past Liberty Hall towards the bus station? He's going in the wrong direction.'

'Dustin Hoffman doesn't know that. He's not from Dublin. Anyway, the car turns around and pulls up outside the Savoy Cinema. Thousands of people are straining at the crush barriers to see him. Cameras flash, women shriek and searchlights probe the sky. The moment arrives. The limousine sidles up beside the red carpet. The rear door slides open and out steps Dustin Hoffman. For the first time, the people see that he's seriously short arsed. They are hugely disappointed. They expect their movie stars to be larger than life. Not squirts. A hush falls over the assembled throng. Don't you think Dustin Hoffman senses that, senses that he has disappointed them? That's what he has to live with. It can't be easy.'

Eddie was sucking on the last centimetre or two of the roll-up. A long finger of ash fell off and lodged in his crotch. He was past caring.

'Maybe that's why they pay him a million dollars a picture. If I was getting that kind of money, I wouldn't care what height I was.'

I looked at him with a benevolence tinged with pity. 'Ah, my son, but you would care. You would care precisely because you are being paid a million dollars a picture. What does a millionaire midget want more than anything else in the world? Because of the very fact he has so much money he wants the only thing that money can't buy. Yes, he yearns for altitude. He wants to be taller. It's about vanity. No man can be a real star without vanity. Even John Wayne had lifts in his shoes, and he was tall to start with. He wore a corset too.'

'John Wayne wouldn't have worn a corset.'

'He was terrified of horses too.'

'How do you know?'

'It's in the same book.'

'That's some book.'

'It certainly is.'

'What else is in it?'

'Audie Murphy killed two hundred Germans.'

'When?'

'When do you think? During the fucking war. Did you think he killed them in Benidorm?'

'Got away with it, did he?'

'He was a war hero.'

'How tall was he?'

'Five feet six inches.'

'Symmetrical face?'

'What else.'

'How tall were the dead Germans?'

'According to the law of averages, most of them would've been taller than him.'

'Must've sneaked up behind them.'

'It's a dirty world.'

'Before he was in the movies, Errol Flynn was a slave trader in New Guinea.'

'How tall was he?'

'Over six feet.'

'How did he get in ahead of the short-arses?'

'I don't know. Robert Mitchum was a hobo.'

'That's not very exotic.'

'Depends on your point of view. Sean Connery polished coffins.'

'Makes you think, doesn't it?'

'There are things out there in the world that we'll never understand.'

'Yeah.'

'Who was Ireland's first cinema manager?'

'Jimmy O'Dea.'

'Close. James Joyce.'

'Now I've heard everything.'

'No, you haven't. Raquel Welch used to be secretary to a bishop.'

'That must have tested His Lordship's faith.'

'Too true.'

'Bishop takes Queen.'

'Checkmate.'

Eddie sighed and reached into his pocket for more cigarette papers. But there wouldn't be time for that. Just as well. The coach shuddered to a halt.

We had arrived at the gig.

16

We were parked outside what looked like a large tin hut. This was not what we'd expected.

'Are you sure this is the right place?' I asked Harpo.

'Yup,' he said, preparing to vacate his seat. 'Saint Bridget's Hall. Enjoy.'

St Bridget's Hall was indeed a tin hut. Largish, long, narrow and decrepit, the kind of place I thought I'd never see again. I thought I had moved on.

All the signs of a hellishly long night were present.

I'd played in plenty of these remote dilapidated country kips when I was starting out, and even with The Chessmen, but Brown and O'Brien was supposed to be a notch above this kind of shite-house.

I heard the screech of O'Brien's brakes as he pulled up behind us. He had been tailing us with Billy and the three women on board.

I stared at the hall. There was the usual flapping panel of rogue asbestos roofing and one or two split panes of glass made good and draught-free by the application of roughly fashioned cardboard squares.

Lashback was peering out the window of the van.

'What the fuck are we doing playing here! Harpo, Are you sure this is where we're supposed to be?

'For the second and final time, yes. This is the gig. Get used to it.'

The hall was built on a rise. A set of a dozen or so concrete steps rose steeply to the main entrance. The square of concrete at the top of the steps was manned by a woman, a solitary crone who greeted our arrival with professional indifference. Or, at least whatever stood there resembled a woman, her blotched bare arms folded across a bosom that consisted of one large über tit that stretched from neck to waist, a sprawling single mammary gland that seemed to slosh about at will inside a stained polka-dotted pinafore that billowed in the stiff evening breeze. Although the light was fading we could see scrawny legs encased in World-War-II nylons that sagged at the knees and gathered about her ankles. Her small feet occupied a remarkable pair of shattered purple bedroom slippers. The solitary lamp at the top of the door illuminated her head from behind, highlighting each strand of witch-like hair, mercifully concealing her face in Hitchcockian shadow.

We'd been parked in front of the hall for a good five minutes before she deigned to waddle down the steps towards the coach, thus providing us with an excellent opportunity to view her spectacular limp. We were connoisseurs of limps, as indeed we were of any physical deformity or oddity borne by the public. It's an interest shared by many other heads, probably a throwback to the bad old days when relief bands were a rarity and a man was expected to stand on stage, bored rigid, from nine in the evening until two o'clock in the morning. Faced by a marathon stretch such as this, a man had no choice but to take an interest in his surroundings to prevent the onset of terminal *ennui*.

A punter with a deformity was a welcome sight. It broke the monotony. His or her progress and *modus operandi* would be casually monitored from the stage. Those who limped badly but danced regardless were particularly welcome, a high degree of chutzpah being required on the part of the afflicted to take to the dance floor at all.

Keen observation of a crippled man struggling to execute the quickstep may not be most people's idea of fun, but we didn't look at it that way. Our choice of occupation more or less dictated that we would become keen students of the human condition.

And it helped to pass the time.

I was more of a proboscis man myself, and spent endless hours scouring the faces of the dancers for the ugliest or largest nose. The triumphant owner was inevitably male.

I still do it today. In idle moments amongst a crowd, I find myself scanning the facial contours of the innocent.

But I digress.

The woman outside Saint Bridget's Hall had been allocated the type of limp that conveyed the impression that she was rushing headlong towards her destination without the ability to halt when required. We had seen this limp before and had categorised it. This was the Speed Limp, fairly rare, and worthy of note. Like the Dropped Arse, it was more often, as was much else, encountered in the west of the country.

There was also the Tumbleweed Limp, the Outwardly-Swinging-Leg Limp and, crucially, the Double-Barrelled Limp which affected, sadly, both legs.

Nevertheless, she did somehow manage to drop anchor when she reached the coach. She mashed her face roughly against one of the side passenger windows. We noted that the glass didn't distort the contours of her blunt, ugly features. The squashed face looked no different then it had before being squashed. Bang goes another natural law.

She waved a hand impatiently and Ray, being adjacent, rolled down one of our windows to accommodate her.

'Are ye the band?' she squawked.

Ray matched her gaze coolly: 'No,' he said smoothly. 'We're the Knights of fucking Malta on our annual outing.'

Harpo appeared swiftly by her side.

'Of course, we're the band. Howerya, luv! Gear goes in the back door, does it, darlin'?' He flashed his cheeky-chappie gap-toothed grin and engaged her in more roadie-speak, which she seemed to understand perfectly well.

'There's no back door worth talking about,' she revealed. 'You'll have to hump it up the steps and in the front.'

Groans from us.

We'd have to help Harpo carry the equipment in.

I contemplated this immediate prospect with little relish and wondered why our management had sent us to play here at all—a two-chip-van band at a one-chip-van venue.

We had long ago discovered that the number of chip vans attendant at any gig was a useful yardstick with which to gauge a band's general popularity. And it wasn't just a matter of the capacity of the hall, although in this case, it was (if you know what I mean). Let me explain.

A hall such as the kip in question could never be more than a one-chip van hall, having a capacity of, let's say, five hundred people. People tend to develop a hunger when they are fired up. Therefore, there are times when a crowd of five hundred people will require two chuck wagons if they are excited at the end of the dance. However, a venue like this would never attract a band capable of exciting a five-hundred-strong crowd to the extent that their appetite would require two chip-vans. This tin hut was accustomed to one-chip van bands.

And that's why we shouldn't be here.

We were punching below our weight. Ordinarily, at most gigs, we attracted crowds of a thousand punters or more and could sometimes excite them so much that as many as four chip vans were required to assuage their false hunger.

And yet here we were, a two-chip-van band (sometimes capable of rising to four) playing in a one-chip-van joint—a travesty. Clear?

And we had to lug the equipment in ourselves.

Sometimes a band could attain the dizzy heights of five or six chip vans but only a Royal Showband at its height in the mid-sixties, or a Drifters, featuring the disturbingly satanic Joe Dolan, could've been guaranteed to summon that kind of burger power. The mind whirled at the thought of six fully functioning chip vans parked in military formation awaiting the onslaught of Galway-Wallop-crazed punters with a powerful lust for greasy fish suppers, Widow's Memories (fat sausages to you) and hockey-puck hamburgers encased in buns that had been blue-moulded prior to toasting.

Who needed pop charts as a guide to a band's popularity? Let the fish-fryers be the judges. Their grease-spattered tills couldn't be wrong.

As a rule, Harpo didn't mind carrying the gear in unaided if the back door led directly to the stage, which was usually the case. Sometimes he had help, often some sullen dysfunctional youth from Belfast who'd washed up in Dublin. We called them Harpettes.

I reckoned there'd be more of these refugees if the Troubles intensified.

However, there were none today, and even Harpo might baulk at the prospect of a dozen steep steps, the negotiation of a narrowish door and who knows what other obstacles, before trailing weighty speakers and amplifiers the length of the dance floor and then schlepping them up onto the distant stage. There was a narrow door at the back of the hall that looked as if it had been custom-made for Wee Mick the celebrated dwarf. It was deemed suitable only for the pissing out of.

Billy and O'Brien, of course, had summed up the situation in a flash, executing a speedy withdrawal with the women in tow, in search of the nearest boozer.

We understood this flight. Men of the calibre of Brown and O'Brien couldn't be expected to be seen performing such a plebeian act as humping band equipment. Too menial and demeaning.

Shallow bastards.

By the time everything was plonked onto the wobbly stage, we were knackered.

When our rasping breath eased and no longer tore at our lungs, we took stock of our surroundings.

The interior of the hall was rectangular, bleak, bare and, of course, the mandatory five degrees cooler than the temperature outside.

Antediluvian chairs lined the two longer walls, and the back of the hall played host to a wooden booth consisting of a linoleum-covered counter behind which stood jerry-built shelves buckling under the weight of many bottles of orangeade with clouded bottoms.

A windowless wall was covered by a mural depicting everyday country life. This was a common sight in rural halls, but this one was special due to the fact that the artist had demonstrated a limited grasp of the concept of scale. The pastoral scene consisted of a farmhouse surrounded by fields in which sturdy men toiled. Also in these fields grazed and pecked sundry animals and birdlife, including cattle, sheep, fowl, geese, ducks, beasts of burden and scattered pigs. Using the central feature of the farmhouse as a yardstick, I calculated that the sheep grazing nearby were at least thirty feet tall. A rearing horse domiciled in the adjoining acreage had somehow attained Tyrannosaurus-Rex proportions, weighing in at, I would say, approximately twenty tons but still, magically, managed to be smaller than the sheep. Six men working nearby were clearly very small midgets indeed, so small as to be practically invisible. A nearby flowing stream had the relative span of a Ganges and a Brobdingnagian child slid happily down a Lilliputian haystack.

The place stank of paraffin oil and the wax that had been applied to the dance floor to enable the gnarled feet of the dancers to glide more smoothly across the surface. Such applications were rare these days. I hadn't come across this for some time and had to slide a tentative foot across the floor to verify this antiquated practice. The words 'fire' and 'risk' were obviously seldom coupled in Saint Bridget's Hall.

I am reminded now of the old petrol-on-the-tie trick (sadly, no longer relevant) which, I had been told, was a common ruse in country dance halls in days of yore. When not many young bucks had access to a car, most walked or pushed a bicycle, but the more adventurous took to sprinkling a drop or two of petrol on their ties. This characteristic odour of fossil fuel would hopefully be ingested by their dancing partners. The matter would be seldom raised or discussed but the females would logically assume, by the olfactory evidence, that the suitor was motorised. This was important at the end of the night when girls' thoughts turned to who would be granted the honour of leaving them home and bestowing, perchance, a kiss, a furtive grope or more. And so what if it turned out that the young man with the smelly tie didn't have a car after all. He hadn't claimed to have wheels, did he? His odour merely suggested it.

Also, it is to be assumed as given that the lad who sprinkled petrol on his tie would be a cautious smoker.

It's comforting to know that a man can buy pheromones by the gallon.

Investigating a tiny, musty room behind the stage, I found it stuffed with detritus from forgotten parish pantomimes and charity concerts. Amongst the smaller varieties of rubbish were major items such as a keyless piano, a bingo machine minus balls, half a trombone, a stringless harp, a plastic bucket with coloured paper stars stuck on it, the remains of a faded but life-sized cigar-store Indian, and a mouldy pile of discarded coloured rags.

This was obviously our dressing room.

A shriek travelled down the hall from the direction of the mineral bar. 'There's tea down here if yese want it!' bellowed the crone.

We filed wearily down to a makeshift kitchen conveniently situated next to the gentleman's toilet. The air was rich with the unusually paired aroma of stewing tea and fortnight-old urine.

The crone was busily buttering slices of white bread, pausing only to wipe her runny nose with the hem of her pinafore.

'Tomatoes OK, boys?'

Nothing like a tomato sandwich to fortify a man faced with a night on his feet on the rickety stage of a draughty, cold, tumbledown shack.

'Thanks fine, luv. Good on ye,' rattled Harpo. 'Expecting a big crowd tonight?'

'No,' she cackled. 'Don't know why we're opening up at all. I didn't know there was going to be a dance here at all tonight until the day before yesterday.'

I stared hard at Harpo. He didn't meet my eye.
Fucking managers.

————

We were set up and badly fed by ten o'clock. I was slightly worried, The
crone had intimated that the hours of the dance were from approximately
ten o'clock to two a.m. Assuming that a relief band had been arranged,
this meant that there was no need for us to go anywhere near the stage
until shortly after midnight. We were psychologically geared to play for
two hours maximum, ninety minutes if we could get away with it.

If, as was unthinkable, a relief group didn't show up, we'd have to
take to the stage very shortly. A four-hour stint. Ten until two would
then become more like Ten to Eternity.

I hadn't played a four- or five-hour dance for years and I didn't like
the look of this place. There was nothing more soul-destroying than
taking to the stage early in a place like this. Firstly, no matter what
season the country was enjoying at the time, the empty venue would be
as cold as a witch's tit. This was particularly hard on the blue fingers of
those who intended to play guitars, not so bad on the reed and brass
men, who could blow a bit of heat into their respective instruments.

The problem was, of course, compounded in winter. There is no
more excruciating pain than that endured by a man forced to apply
an icy hand topped by numbed fingertips onto the taut slivers of
hard, freezing steel stretched upon a guitar. Upon initial contact, the
numbness disappears instantly, substituted by a searing pain shooting
through the digits, made worse by having to continually slide one's
fingers up and down the fret-board. It's like being carved by cheese-
wire. And the agony does not abate as the night progresses and the
temperature invariably fails to rise.

One also had to contend with Icy Foot Syndrome. During the seventies everyone was six inches taller that they had any right to be, due
to the widespread popularity of platform boots for men. How did we
ever adjust to returning to our god-given natural height when another
cruel twist of fashion forced us to step down from our boots and don
more comfortable but, alas, levelling and undeniably confidence-sapping

footwear? How did we cope with becoming shorter overnight, especially when women remained at their usual altitude?

One must, of course, pay a heavy price for the privilege of looking taller. Most men displayed a brave face by valiantly trying to disguise the fact that they were experiencing some difficulty in walking.

During winter, showband heads playing four- and five-hour dances paid double the price for being taller than nature intended. Firstly, at the beginning of any dance, one had to stand onstage in painfully high-heels for two to three hours, usually burdened by exceptionally heavy electric guitars. Due to the extreme cold and the unnatural arching of one's instep demanded by the high heel, one soon lost all feeling in either peg. Jumping from foot to foot made little difference. It was all one could do to prevent oneself toppling over. Then, during the final two hours, by which time a crowd may or may not have turned up, one was forced to do the Showband Steps, a raggle-taggle collection of communal moves and shapes that evolved over the short history of the genre, most of the routines having been initiated by Dickie Rock, and may he roast in Hell for it.

The rest of one's body, medically known as the trunk, had long since given up. Clad in thin white shirt and lightweight mohair suit, one was already experiencing something akin to the despair that drove Captain Oates to take his final open-ended walk. The initial shivering soon subsided to be replaced by a dull gnawing at the bones that, steadily and relentlessly, chipped at one's will to live.

The flint-faced men who owned country ballrooms usually considered money spent on heating as money pissed away, reasoning that a crowd would heat itself up when it materialised, a large, closely-packed mass of eager and frequently unwashed humanity usually generating all the heat that would be required for the continuance of life. The social anthropologists amongst you will recognise this as the Eskimo Principle.

Only during extreme winter conditions, when failure to provide a rudimentary form of heating stopped only a hair short of genocide, did the ballroom proprietor turn his hand to the task. The solution was often worse than the initial problem. I refer of course to what I know only as the Jet Heater. The man who invented these contraptions should hang his head in shame. The Jet Heater resembled the type of engine one often observes dangling from the wings of large aircraft. Indeed, I do believe both devices operated on similar principles. The Jet Heater is basically a large, high-powered blowtorch.

Placed at the back of the hall where it would be kick-started by a dogsbody, it would then roar and spit until it gathered whatever raw energy was required to fulfil its function, that function being to expel extremely hot air from its round fiery maw. For a number of reasons, I have always been frightened of the Jet Heater.

When one enters a dance hall in Mid-January after climbing with aching limbs from an icicle-kissed van, the roar of the Jet Heater seems enticing. One is often tempted to approach this God-given source of comfort. Maybe even stand in front of it in a bid to heat and revive one's frozen arse. Do not do this. It will singe your trousers and incinerate your balls. There is nothing worse than being simultaneously frozen and burnt. The brain can't process such confusing messages.

Theoretically, the Jet Heater is supposed to raise the general temperature within an enclosed space. For some reason, which I have never succeeded in working out, the machine seems to have the opposite effect. One is invariably colder because the Jet Heater, inexplicably, succeeds in warming only certain pockets of air. One therefore wanders innocently from a freezing area, say near the mineral bar, to a heated area, say outside the ladies toilet. This extreme variation in temperature within a relatively small area confuses the body and urges it to shut down. This puzzles and frustrates.

The Jet Heater also sucks all breathable air from the hall, leaving one to process through one's lungs an evil-smelling, gasoline-tinged vapour of questionable efficacy.

I know that someday in the near future, after a routine medical check, I will be summoned to a hospital where a white-coated man will frown and squint as he raises an X-ray to the light.

He'll ask me to sit whilst he explains that an inexplicable growth has turned up on my chart, a growth that he can neither isolate nor identify. He will tell me that it is unlike anything he has ever encountered before. He will say that it appears to be something that has lain dormant for a number of years.

I will then tell him about the Jet Heater.

But I digress, again.

Jesus, I thought to myself, this is like a gig where there will be no fucking relief band at all—a fate we seldom contemplated of late. The system worked like this. No agricultural dancing punter in his or her right mind would come to a dance until the pubs were closed and emptied, all the dance halls being traditionally dry. Catholic Ireland had decreed that the shitkickers, sorry, patrons, previously content dancing at De Valera's crossroads but who had now shifted indoors, would be denied the solace of an alcoholic beverage. In practice, this meant that nobody but the village idiot or the local deranged spinster appeared in any country dance hall much before midnight.

To the uninitiated this may seem to make little tangible difference to bands such as ours, rendering the presence of a relief band unnecessary. And this would indeed have been the case if it hadn't been for... 'People Who Sit Outside In Their Cars'.

'People Who Sit Outside In Their Cars' have been the plague of every head who has ever yearned for peace to drink a bottle of stout whilst waiting for the rabble to gather.

Let me explain. One must assume that, apart from our dance in Saint Bridget's Hall that night, there would very probably have been another dance taking place in another hall within a five-mile radius.

The 'People Who Sit Outside In Their Cars' were the people who had not yet decided which of these dances they would attend. Also, they did not seem interested in drinking whisky or stout. They must therefore be regarded as dysfunctional—witness their foolish practice of turning up early, indicating the absence of a life bursting to be lived to the full.

If no relief band showed up, the following conversation would take place somewhere in the vicinity of the band.

'It's ten past ten, boys. Time you were on the stage,' the crone, or the owner of the hall, would announce.

'But there'll be nobody in here until after midnight,' one of us would rightly point out.

'They'll be outside listening in their cars,' the witch or warlock would crow.

'Who will?' we would say, feigning ignorance.

'The people who won't be paying to come in.'

That's the way it usually went. It's the Lemming Syndrome. There was a time I was used to it.

People who showed up in a car outside a dance hall at ten o'clock at night were also insecure. When there were two dances going on simultaneously in one particular area it seemed obvious that the most well known and popular band would automatically draw the biggest crowd. It was a natural law. The way show business worked in those days. These punters didn't seem to know this.

A number of cars, often many, would arrive outside one of the functioning dance halls. There might be as many as five passengers aboard each vehicle. They would remain within their vehicles ostensibly listening to the band. They would expect this band to have already started to play, despite an absence of paying customers.

But they were not really listening to the band at all. They were, instead, watching the other cars to see if those vehicles would show any sign of transferring allegiance to the rival dance hall. When some of the cars did eventually leave, the others would follow, on the grounds that the faithless departed may know something they don't, so let's not linger. If no music emanated from the other hall, the posse would return to their original stakeout and sit a while longer. This cat-and-mouse exercise might be repeated two or three times and last for up to two hours until, usually about midnight, a snap decision was made by the occupants of one group of cars to abandon their vehicles and enter the chosen dance hall. The others would follow. Lemmings all. The ritual was over.

Nobody really knew how this system worked. Just as no-one really knows how Siberian geese find their way to mudflats in Donegal, none of us heads knew what triggered a decision to choose one dance hall and reject another. There seemed to be no criteria. And remember that the eventual choice of venue had fuck-all to do with the quality of music heard seeping through the walls. A mere din would suffice. Hence the relief groups.

A ritual as old as time itself. Akin to the crawling up a tropical beach by sea-going turtles whose predecessors have deposited their peeled eggs on the same stretch of sand for countless millennia.

Nobody questioned the judgment of the 'People Who Sit Outside In Their Cars'.

It was just the way life was then. I blame the education system.

This was why most bands employed relief bands to provide a comforting din for the waverers outside. The price for not doing so would be an empty car park, no chip vans, an ill-attended gig and the forfeiture of a considerable portion of the night's agreed fee or the previously negotiated percentage of readies lifted at the door.

And why else would a band take the risk of not being paid for not playing to nobody?

———

There was no need for alarm. Our relief band showed up just after we'd hoovered up the tomato sandwiches.

There were four of them in all, average age, approximately nineteen. They had the usual bad attitude. I spotted the troublemaker right away. There was always one. Even the Beatles had John Lennon. This one had little round glasses too, a spotty face and a Bob Dylan cap. Risqué for Donegal.

I was onstage fiddling with my guitar when I felt them gather behind me.

'There you go, lads. You the band?' I shouted cheerily. I knew not to use the word 'relief'. I knew from experience that some of them didn't like it.

Problem was that most of the relief bands didn't have much respect for showbands, having correctly come to the conclusion that most comprised arrogant arseholes, bluffers and spivs.

And they had probably suffered in the past from not being aware of Show Business Rule Number 14, i.e. showbands who are shite will invariably treat those lower down the totem pole like shite too. Because they had no reason to assume that we were any different, these young lads, displayed well, an attitude. I chide myself for thinking of them as young lads but, then again, I am aware that at twenty-eight, I was an ancient in their eyes.

And, of course, there's nothing wrong with having an attitude. It's the rock upon which rock 'n' roll was founded—what rock 'n' roll has always been about. The spottier the better and fuck everybody else.

But it was hard to take in a place like Donegal.

And we weren't like the others.

'We won't be needing your lead guitar's amp,' Spotty snapped. 'I'll use my own.' He was wearing the kind of denim jacket and jeans that can't be bought in cities and can only be found in the villages and small towns of Ireland; that exclusive Eastern European look. The other three were similarly kitted out but had the good sense to look embarrassed about it.

Relief bands who preferred to use their own equipment were extremely annoying in principle. We, as the main attraction, were expected to facilitate and put all ours at their disposal, except, for arcane reasons, as drummers were quick to claim, the allegedly fragile snare drum.

This arrangement was both magnanimous and practical as it prevented confusion and awkwardness when the bands changed over onstage. The main attraction could not linger whilst relief groups wrapped up their own pathetic bits of electrical equipment and dragged them offstage. The job of a relief group was to play until told to stop and then fuck off smartly.

Spotty, however, had deemed Eddie's amp not good enough for his purposes. Eddie's equipment was, of course, of the highest quality and more than adequate.

Spotty was, to use a musical expression, acting the cunt.

Oh, I reflected, if only George were here. George had played trumpet with The Chessmen during the golden days when we were on our last legs and enjoyed the glorious floating feeling of caring little about anything because nothing mattered any more. He hated relief groups with a passion bordering on the criminal. He was also an accomplished electrician, proficient at constructing complicated gadgets and gizmos that would perform intricate and often dangerous functions.

George would've smiled sweetly at Spotty and offered to help him rig up the equipment in question. George would then have covertly and expertly placed a short length of copper wire deep within the innards of the amplifier, taking care that it carefully straddled two vital electrical points, terminals or whatever they're called.

All would seem normal and shipshape when Spotty plugged in. His equipment would work perfectly well until the copper wire, as it was supposed to, consumed itself, and by doing so broke some manner of complicated connection, thus causing something dreadful to happen between the two aforementioned electrical terminals. Approximately one hour into the relief group's set, a small muffled, internal explosion would render Spotty's amplifier useless and cause it to catch fire. An alarming development in an enclosed space.

By this juncture, George and the rest of us would be settled in the nearest pub. In the fullness of time, an emissary belonging to the group would probably be sent to find us. He would inform us that Spotty's amplifier had mysteriously blown up and ignited and would it be all right if he used Eddie's amp after all and would we perhaps send some-one back to the hall to arrange same?

He would then be told to fuck off.

That's the way to treat them. Make sure they don't forget who they tangled with.

But we didn't work that way anymore.

Probably because we were too worn out to be nasty.

——

We could hear the sickening crunch of out-of-tune guitars and the juvenile yelps of the relief band beginning to bounce off the stone walls as we thankfully left the empty hall and clambered into the van.

There were People Sitting Outside In Their Cars.

They gazed dully at us without seeming to see us. We knew well that the Bovine Stare was best ignored.

Harpo was left behind in the hall to supervise proceedings. Pat opted to keep Harpo company, a thankless task, though, to his mind, probably infinitely preferable to having to tolerate us for a few unnecessary hours. Additionally, Harpo was left behind because it seemed a good idea at the time and he tended to be boring in pubs. But not because we disapproved of roadies drinking. *Au contraire*, we adopted what I considered an enlightened attitude towards those who drink and subsequently drive. Roadies capable of driving long distances whilst intoxicated were seen as custodians of a rare talent and, as such, much sought after as long as they didn't start drinking too early in the day. Those who were drunk too early ran the risk of the alcohol prematurely dying in them, thereby rendering them prematurely sober, tired and argumentative. Roadies should never start drinking until midnight. If drunk by two o'clock in the morning, they can, with the occasional top-up and someone in the passenger seat to talk to, keep going more or less indefinitely. There is an art in talking to roadies who are faced with the prospect of driving all night whilst reasonably drunk.

Due to recurring nightmares featuring shattered glass, blood-curdling screams and twisted metal, I found it almost impossible to nod off in a speeding coach, I usually took up the Talking Seat. Most heads tend to avoid this front passenger seat beside the driver because they usually regard roadies as mentally retarded or worse. I didn't mind occupying it when duty beckoned, particularly when the battery expired in my miner's helmet, effectively ruling out further reading. Given that set of circumstances, I didn't mind talking to driving roadies, especially as the probable alternative was that they might fall asleep and kill all on board.

Most roadies then were men who wanted to become musicians but hadn't the patience nor the wit to sit down and learn how to play an instrument, or didn't attempt it because they feared failure. Encouragingly and mercifully, I never met one who wanted to become a singer.

They all, of course, adored music and, to a lesser extent, musicians. Most were in their early- to late-thirties, wore their hair in pony tails and were frequently tattooed. Many I had encountered over the years seemed to experience difficulty sustaining normal conversations, often inexplicably drying up at crucial moments, preferring instead to tell long, complicated, dirty jokes—traditionally the last refuge of the thwarted or wounded.

And nearly all had trouble establishing meaningful relationships with women. One of my past roadie confidants once told me that he loved women but didn't know what to do with them after he'd fucked them.

I suggested that he talk to them occasionally, to which he replied, 'What about?'

His was a complicated case requiring the kind of time and concentrated care that is generally available only in the private sector.

I found that roadies, in general, liked talking about their childhoods, happier times when things were simpler, life looked brighter and disappointments were fewer.

They realised fully there was no long-term future in being a roadie, aware that they were going nowhere fast and would probably end up renting a small farmhouse in Mayo where they would harvest magic mushrooms, listen to Pink Floyd albums until the records or the listener disintegrated, and maintain a brace of goats. Maybe buy a high-powered motorcycle to alarm the bumpkins.

Many of them were inordinately interested in group sex and often tried to arrange same with the small camp-following of rides who tailed each popular showband. Even seasoned rides tended to baulk at this unless members of the band were involved. And even the Woodentops were fussy about who gangbanged them. The Summer of Love had come (if you excuse the expression) and gone. There were a lot of freaks still about and a girl couldn't be too careful.

Roadies also liked talking about cowboy movies. Usually *Shane* or *The Magnificent Seven*. Sometimes both during a long night. Few of them cared for *High Noon* on a visceral level, suspecting that Gary Cooper would've preferred to have high-tailed it out of town.

I once riled one of them by suggesting that in *Shane*, Alan Ladd had no need to theatrically twirl his gun after killing Jack Palance. He argued that it was necessary as a statement of finality—closure, we call it now.

I called it show business, a circus trick. We agreed to disagree. His commitment to Alan Ladd was frightening. He didn't believe me when I told him that Alan Ladd was one of the short-arsed movie stars who eventually drank themselves to death in the Hollywood Hills. Nor did he like Van Heflin, even when told that Mr Heflin was quite tall and had a metal plate in his head, or maybe that was Van Johnson.

They all wanted to be Steve McQueen.

Motorcycles again.

But back to the drink.

In the show-band seventies there was no such thing as snatching car keys from a man because he had drink taken. Too totalitarian. A man was considered to be in charge of his own destiny. If he wanted to drive when seriously pissed, he was granted the benefit of the doubt. It was assumed that he knew what he was doing.

Confiscating a man's car keys for his own good is a relatively modern concept and contrary to our way of thinking at the time. It was like asking Jack Palance to hand in his gun.

Modern thinking behind the condemnation of excessive alcohol consumption prior to driving a car is based on the assumption that the driver will be unaware that drink is impairing his ability to drive—the vision of an innocent slumped behind the wheel.

I consider this assumption degrading and erroneous. Let's give drunken drivers the credit to which they are entitled. These men are adults and have passed disparate tests.

Experienced drunken drivers are fully aware that, if they drive too quickly, they will be killed and may also kill others to whom they have not been introduced. That is why the majority of drunks drive carefully and travel at a reasonably slow rate of knots. Most reasonable and intelligent men who are drunk will drive a car with the care and consideration of the average nun. They have little choice. Their lives depend on it.

The small minority who speed whilst drunk are generally the kind of people who are first to volunteer for service when wars are declared. They are not generally missed when they are eventually killed in action.

17

We spotted O'Brien's Mercedes outside what did indeed appear to be licensed premises a mile or two up the road at a crossroads from which, according to the four arms of the signpost, one could travel to Letterkenny, Malin Head, Gweedore or Donegal Town. Being familiar with these parts I noticed that the signpost, of course, had been skewed round the wrong way by helpful locals, standard practice in Donegal. The stranger motoring to Letterkenny will find himself on the road to Gweedore, the Letterkenny traveller to Malin Head etc. *ad infinitum.*

Annoying for the stranger but a little hard-earned revenge for the disaffected perpetrators.

No other vehicle but the Merc was parked outside so we swung the coach as near to the door as possible. No point in walking further than was strictly necessary.

I liked these country pubs. There was fun to be had if a man kept his head.

To the uninitiated, the absence of cars outside might have seemed at odds with the bustling throng within.

Morality Tale
Show Business Lesson Number Two
Never Show Weakness in a Country Pub. The Locals Will Sense it
and Destroy You

Showband heads must take care when they visit country pubs for the purpose of whiling away time before a gig. Let us remind ourselves that pubs in 1972 were not the smokeless, prawn-cocktailed dentists' waiting rooms into which they have now evolved. These isolated watering-holes were places were real men came to drink, smoke, spit on the floor, talk about hurling, tell lies about women and discuss livestock. The last thing they wanted to see was the arrival of a bunch of city-born nancy boys with painted doxies tripping behind them.

A head therefore required nerves of steel. There is a fine line between good-natured banter from the indigenous population and the murmured insult that might conceivably lead to unpleasantness and a quick burst of fisticuffs.

The average head was normally despised and secretly envied by the locals in roughly equal measure. We must remember that this was before the majority of Irish people had any sense of their own worth. The average rural young man in a pub would like as not harbour a fairly substantial chip on his shoulder, especially if he had spent quality time wearing a blue suit in the Irish clubs in England and miserable months with a hod on that same overcrowded shoulder. This tends to create a form of simmering bitterness that reacts badly to the sight of men from unknown corners of his country acting as if they own his local.

Unless you were a show-business person openly admired by the agricultural community and accepted as one of their own, e.g. the Larry Cunninghams and Big Toms of this world, or a semi-city boy who was obviously wholesome, flawless and good, e.g. the Brendans O'Brien and Bowyer (of the Dixielanders and Royal showbands respectively), there was little hope of acceptance. The average drinker in a rural Irish pub had little understanding of, or time for, whey-faced, skinny-legged, long-haired runts who often seemed on the verge of imminent physical collapse.

A display of confidence was vital. As I say, there was fun to be had if a head kept his head. The idea was somehow to win the locals over right away. A way had to be found to win immediate and unconditional acceptance so that one might relax. And, as it was impossible for the likes of us to pretend that we and the people we encountered in these pubs were as one, we often had to, well, dazzle them.

There were a number of ways this could be achieved.

I have always been an admirer of the Concentrated Solo Effort. The man who introduced this concept is known to me but I shall not divulge his identity on the grounds that he may no longer appreciate his name being linked to it. This is understandable. Men grow older and change for the worse.

I must, however, doff my hat to this man for providing many hours of endless fun for heads and moments of confused inadequacy for local drinkers in remote public houses.

He knows who he is.

Head A, as I shall dub him, had a harem of stunning women scattered about the country. Such was his thoroughness that no matter where the gig, he would be no further than forty miles from a long-legged woman of great pulchritude. A singer, of course, he went for dark-haired, hour-glass-figured, mightily-titted types whom he would scoop up from their homes in his flashy car (he, of course, never travelled with the lads in the band). He would insist that these women wore revealing outfits when seen with him on the grounds that he wanted other men to see as much as possible of what they could not have. Nor did he drink. A teetotaller, the procurement and enjoyment of sex was his life and alcohol had no part to play in it. Most serious sex addicts are sober men. When he arrived at a gig with one of his scantily-clad women he would instruct her to make her way alone to the nearest pub whilst he busied himself within the confines of the dance hall—sound checks and other sundry tasks.

Meanwhile this beauty would quietly enter a pre-arranged pub alone and gracefully mount a barstool, watched open-jawed by the drooling local clientèle. She would look straight ahead, communicating only to order a soft drink. Otherwise she would speak to or look at no-one.

Imagine the eyes of the locals gazing and feasting upon the flesh of this unattainable creature. None of the locals would approach her, of course. To do so would require a rash confidence of the highest order. And a resultant embarrassing public rejection of this magnitude would be cast up to a dejected man until the day he died, or married (the latter being the more unlikely occurrence).

After some time, Head A would enter the pub, nod meekly as drained faces turned towards his. He would take no notice of the woman sitting on the bar stool and take a seat as far away from her as possible. This would puzzle the locals. As soon as they lamped him coming through the door, they would assume that this unattainable woman was merely biding her time waiting for this stranger. That this did not seem to be the case succeeded in confusing them.

Head A would then order a glass of orange juice and proceed to read a newspaper which he would produce from the roomy pocket of his ragged but stylish sheepskin coat, the only one within a hundred miles (the sheepskin coat, not the newspaper).

A form of Mexican standoff would occur. The eyes of the locals would dart from strange man to long-legged woman, and from woman to man again.

Allowing a considerable period of time to lapse, Head A would slowly put down his newspaper and stare fixedly at the woman, as if seeing her for the first time.

He would then slowly smile and look her up and down in an openly leering and lecherous manner, occasioning a twinge of embarrassment amongst the clientèle, most of whom would be by now almost catatonic with suspense.

Head A would address her across the expanse of bar-room floor.

'Excuse me, honey,' he'd say, quite loudly.

The clientèle would hush further.

All eyes would swivel.

Again.

'I said, excuse me!'

The lady would revolve slowly on her seat, eventually locating the source of the inquiry.

'Are you talking to me, sir?' she would reply.

'I am, indeed.'

She would narrow her eyes and look to the floor.

'May I ask you a question?' he would say.

'If you must.'

'How would you like a good fuck?'

Every yokel held his breath.

The woman would lift her bag, dismount from the bar stool and stride purposefully towards the strange man.

Grown men would cover their eyes, anticipating the worst.

The strange man would get to his feet as the woman approached.

Now it would surely hit the fan.

'Don't mind if I do,' sez she with a preppy grin.

The two of them would then link arms and swiftly vacate the premises.

Imagine the silence that would descend on the disconsolate clump of frustrated men. They had had a glimpse of the way they had always wanted the world to be. They had paid a visit to their wildest dreams.

The happy couple would, reputedly post-coital of course, reappear in the pub later with other members of the band.

And would be treated like gods.

Then, of course, there was the 'I'll-Drink-You–Under-The-Table' manoeuvre. I first came across this by accident in a pub opposite the Flamingo Ballroom in Ballymena, a fabled hall run by the flamboyant and now-departed Sammy Barr. Sammy ran a tight ship and was inordinately proud of his establishment, and particularly obsessed by the self-perceived superior quality of the hot dogs that he personally prepared and served to the bands, hovering like a mother hen whilst these frankfurter depth-charges were experimentally nibbled by men who didn't want them.

'How d'ye like ma hot-dogs, boyz?' was the constant enquiry. We always rubbed our tums and made the expected pleasurable noises.

He was also prone to inform anyone who cared to listen that the Flamingo was the only ballroom in Ireland ever to play host to the Rolling Stones. This was a very big deal indeed in 1970.

We assumed that one Ballymena ballroom had been more than enough for Mick Jagger and the lads. One can imagine Jagger's après-gig conversation with the runtish Andrew Loog-Oldham or whoever it was who managed the band then:

'Right! That's fucking it! No more of these!'

Our gig in the Flamingo was a lunchtime session for BBC Radio One. This was also regarded as a very big deal indeed. A fourth-rate disc jockey who daren't refuse to make the trip was dispatched to Northern Ireland for the purpose of broadcasting live to the British nation from one of its troubled colonies, preferably well away from disaffected areas. Ballymena was a bastion of Loyalism and therefore conveniently devoid of too many troublesome Catholics. Perfect. A crowd would gather to see the zany deejay spin his records, competitions would produce tacky prizes and a local band would be allowed to play two songs live.

To appear at a Radio One Lunchtime Roadshow was regarded as somewhat of a coup. We, of course, were long past that kind of thing. Our days of sucking up to fourth-rate Radio One deejays were over, those days having been few to begin with. The deejay was the usual out-going arsehole, false, jocular and medallion-festooned. I suppose it wasn't his fault that we weren't in the mood for his wholesome banter. We had spent the night travelling in the van, having left Cork City at approximately four in the morning and were therefore not in the greatest physical condition (nor, I must admit, had we been when the journey began) when we arrived for a sound check and run through at eleven o'clock at the other end of the country.

Fortunately we'd had the foresight to assemble a number of sustaining substances and inhalers in anticipation of the rigours of this extended day. The majority decided to run with the substances. I preferred the inhalers because I like to know what I'm dealing with. Introducing the contents of half-a-dozen of them into my system, I knew that six was a tad reckless on a stomach that had been empty for nigh on twenty-four hours, but I was confident I could cope.

We struggled through the gig without too much going wrong and adjourned to the pub opposite the Flamingo. It contained a number of pig farmers on the batter. They were loud, red-faced, stout-limbed and thick. Ulster Scots to a man. As well as Radio One Day in Ballymena it was also Fair Day—as old as the Plantation itself.

All but me were still wearing our black velvet suits, green ruffled shirts and red boots (yes, I know it was only radio but one wore a band suit when appearing in front of an audience. That was the deal), the cause of a certain amount of ribaldry when we entered and ordered pints all round.

The rest of the band were having, unusually, but the one drink to wet the whistle, as they planned to drive straight back to Dublin and had no intention of hanging about these alien parts. I had discovered that I could get a bus to Derry later on that afternoon and had therefore taken the precaution of changing back into my street clothes before I entered the pub. The lads would change their clothes in the van on the way home.

The band soon piled back into the van and headed southwards, leaving me sitting alone at the bar. I had nowhere else to go.

One of the pig farmers approached.

'You dinnae hae wan o' them wee monkey suits tae wear, then?'

'As a matter of fact I have. I just don't choose to wear it all day long.'

He turned to the other shit-kickers.

'He disnae choose to wear it all day looong!' he mimicked, in a plummy voice.

Bastard.

A roar of laughter bounced against the false rafters.

I felt very high. The benzedrine was really kicking in now. I knew I'd taken too much. I could feel every hair tingling in my scalp, my teeth grinding together with alarming force I could feel something shooting up my spine that was not unpleasant.

I felt I had the energy to run up a vertical wall of some considerable height.

I also felt the hot breath of a pig farmer on my neck.

'What's that ye're drinkin' boy?' he leered.

'It's a glass of Harp,' I said, delicately holding up the grimy glass for his inspection.

He didn't look at it at all.

He rubbed the stubble on his chin theatrically.

'Would you no' take a real man's drink?'

I turned and met his rheumy eye with my own glassy globes. The implication was clear.

'And what would that be?'

He winked at his mates.

'Wud ye no' tak a large whiskey?'

'Thank you, very much. If you're buying, I do believe I will.'

A large Jameson appeared.

'And you?' I asked.

'Ah'll hae the same.'

Coins clattered onto the counter.

It was who-can-piss-higher-up-the-wall time. I realised that something competitive had now been initiated. I knew these people. These were Davy Crockett's cousins, the spawn of the relatives John Wayne had left behind. Also, I somehow knew that nothing could hurt me. I was ready for these bastards. No task or trial was beyond me this day. It was the Benzedrine doing its filthy work.

After all, that's what it was for.

I knocked the double whiskey back in one and resumed the civilised sipping of my glass of Harp. I felt fearless. I wasn't really an industrial drinker but something told me to fear nothing this day.

I impulsively ordered another round of double whiskeys and necked mine, again in one.

The pig farmer hadn't finished the first depth-charge and seemed slightly startled by my apparent thirst.

I smacked my lips. 'Your round, I believe?'

And so it went on. Never having previously consumed too much alcohol on top of the inhalers, I was unsure of the ultimate consequences.

As the doubles flowed I realised that, as I had suspected, the Benzedrine was cancelling out the whiskey. I was still absolutely sober after six large whiskeys on an empty stomach.

I could see that the pig farmer was struggling a little. His mates had grown somewhat quiet.

I decided to go for broke.

'Triples from now on, barman,' I announced.

By the time the pig farmer buckled, we'd each drank a bottle of whiskey in one hour. That is usually enough alcohol to merit one a bed in the local A&E. I felt fine. The benzedrine was still shielding me from inebriation.

The game was over when the pig farmer bolted for the toilet.

His mates looked at me with something approaching respect.

I looked at my watch and said to nobody in particular, 'I have a bus to catch but I don't think I'll bother. I'll walk to Derry.'

I strode from the bar and marched up the street, planning to hitchhike. I felt wonderful and soon cadged a lift in what seemed the right direction. I was home by eight o'clock that night.

I collapsed at nine and was unconscious for two days. My mother phoned for a doctor but he didn't come.

I woke up eventually and didn't fully recover for a week.

My digestive system was shot.

Benzedrine and whiskey.

Makes a man feel great even though he's incapable of getting drunk or having sex.

Benzedrine, surely a chemical inspired, invented and condoned by a prankster God.

———

Ray was first to the bar and already had a vodka and coke in his hand before we'd had a chance to case the place. It wasn't too bad as these kips went and I had already spotted Billy and O'Brien in the snug with the three women. The bar was surprisingly deserted save for the usual clump of sullen, ungainly youths and the mandatory old man sitting at the far end of the bar counter, strategically placed with his back to the door of the gentleman's jacks.

I wandered over to the halfish-door of the snug and leant upon it. I could see that Billy was playing the Art Card. Propped on the table and steadied by his elegant hand was the painting that he had picked up in Belfast: looked like a water-colour, some vista in the calm folds of the Glens of Antrim, probably by some MacAuley or other. The scene depicted was that of the standard cattle-encircled gushing brook, fringed by stunted trees whilst the usual expansive vista stretched to the horizon. Could've been worse. Could've been something by the Tory Island Primitives. After all, we weren't too far from their bailiwick.

Billy was riffing the usual bollocks about how well the artist had captured the light and the late-evening colours of an autumnal day. He knew this spiel. He believed in art and enjoyed talking about it whilst at the same time being clinically aware of the effect it had on women. The three charvers were hanging on to every syllable that slipped from his lips. Let Mother Ireland never allow us to forget how women melt when talked to on an equal level by a good-looking, well-known, sensitive, wealthy man who could articulate his concept of art and beauty and wished to share it with them. Bosoms heaved and legs were involuntarily crossed.

O'Brien could've talked like that too, if he'd wanted to. He was something of a connoisseur himself, in a different though no-less-desirable field, as far as women were concerned. He knew his way around gold, silver, general jewellery—the money stuff. As a teenager he had spent time as either an apprentice goldsmith or jeweller, but there was little need for any input from him now, apart from the occasional gap-toothed winning smile and a timely nod of assent. Billy was doing a good enough solo job of enthralling the women. Doing the heavy lifting, as it were.

All O'Brien had to do was listen, smile and fuck one of the women later... maybe two.

Because there was, of course, a spare, a fact noted by Ray who duly appeared beside me, again stroking his beard rhythmically, sporting the greasy grin that he employed when he figured he was in with a chance.

He entered the snug and pulled up a stool beside the unclaimed charver, who, although a little mousy and on the wrong side of plump, was just about within his pulling range. As far as looks went, Ray always reminded me of an undernourished, bipedal, unkempt rodent. This did not seem to hinder him. It was unusual for Ray to stay within his capabilities when it came to hitting on women. Supremely assured, he always zoomed in on the stunners. In others, a ploy such as this might conceivably pay off, as a raffish confidence without any obvious basis often engenders a degree of curiosity in the female of the species. Additionally, it normally buys a little time during which a man may give it his best shot.

This is when Ray usually crashed and burned. In the short time allotted to him because of his brash manner, he usually managed to display no charm and even less personality.

If he'd been a normal being I would've felt sorry for him.

He was on a winner this time though. The mousey one was glad to be hit on by anybody.

Billy's was the brightest spark, blonde, brassy and up for it. The one sectioned off by O'Brien was plainer, dark and not unappealing in a rough kind of way.

Ray was lumbered with the gooseberry.

They suited each other.

I left them to it and joined Eddie and Lashback who were sitting at the bar being stared at by the local youths.

Lashback was sitting too close to the locals and I could tell by his bulging eyes that it would take very little to upset him. He was outwardly relaxed but the furtive darting about of his mincers relayed the suspicion that all was not well beneath the surface. The internal cauldron was bubbling.

The local youths were already sniggering amongst themselves in that shy but insidious manner that often precedes a punch-up.

I fussed about and got the two of them shifted to the other end of the bar directly opposite the old man guarding the toilet.

The barman was of standard appearance, red-headed, skinny and mean-spirited. He watched us carefully through narrowed eyelids.

I looked at no-one, lit a cigarette and stared at the old coffin-dodger. He smiled a thin smile and locked back into whatever thoughts had occupied him before he noticed us obstructing his view of the middle distance.

A comfortable silence fell between the three of us, the kind of unembarrassed silence familiar to married couples of long-standing.

My mother and father were like that. Never seemed to have a proper conversation. Just a gruff exchange of those pieces of essential information vital for the continuation of a well-ordered, simple but comfortable life. People who've been together for a long time don't need to talk to each other. Previous generations understood this. We don't seem to.

Instead of resigning ourselves to our individual choices, we 'fall out of love' and get divorced.

I wondered how long I could stay with this band, how long could I put up with worse-than-useless nights like these, marooned in the bowels of nowhere, wasting time and keeping a weather eye on a bunch of testosterone-maddened yokels. But, then again, who was I to complain? At least I was not a 'freedom fighter', like a significant proportion of the people with whom I went to school. Poor misguided bastards. Now, there was a gig going nowhere, I thought.

Eddie was reflective too, absentmindedly twirling a rogue lock of hair with a curled forefinger.

'I think you're right. I think Billy's charver, the one with the tits, I think she does look like Mabel.'

'Ya think so?' I murmured.

Lashback displayed a flicker of interest.

'I asked you fuckers about her before but you wouldn't tell me. Who is she?'

'A special woman,' said Eddie, sipping at something yellowish, 'Too rich for your blood.'

'Not too far away, either. Ballyshannon,' I rejoined. 'A matter of a few short miles.'

'She's long gone out of there,' said Eddie.

'I know.'

Lashback was beginning to get annoyed. The dark circles under his eyes had developed pale patches. Blotchy.

'But who the fuck was she and what was so special about her.'

'A horsey woman,' I said. 'And enthusiastic dominatrix.'

'A wha'?' enquired Lashback.

'A horsey woman.'

'No, the other thing.'

'A dominatrix.'

'What's that when you're at home?'

'A dominatrix.' I spoke slowly now. 'The dominant woman partner in a sadomasochistic relationship.'

Lashback looked at me blankly.

'A rough mot,' I summarised.

'Why didn't you say that in the first place?'

Why not indeed?

18

Final Morality Tale
Show Business Lesson Number Three
Try Each Thing Once. It May Not Come Your Way Again

Bundoran is a seaside resort where, in the seventies, anything went and human life was rapidly becoming cheapish. This was mainly due to the influx of earnest but cautious 'freedom fighters' from the North who had chosen the town as the location of their current residence of choice, not because of the invigorating sea air, but mainly due to the absence of the British Army and an RUC who had resolved to hunt them down like dogs. The Garda Síochána remained stoically detached.

Eddie and I were familiar with the area. I first became aware of the peculiarities of the town when I went on my first Southern trip with a band. I was barely seventeen. A gather-up band that shall be, or, come to think of it, actually was, nameless, we made a point of visiting Bundoran even though our gig that night was way off track in the Midlands somewhere. I soon realised why, when I saw a chain of showband vans parked outside a local chemist's shop. The Appointed One from each band of minstrels would enter the pharmacy and re-emerge with an adequate supply of selected uppers and downers. All designed to put a spring in a man's step or, indeed, render him comatose, a matter of personal choice. This was like pulling in for a fill-up at a petrol station.

It was therefore highly appropriate that this was where we should encounter Mabel. Although we had originally been after her daughter, Helen, a beautiful, willowy, exotically English rose of some nineteen or twenty summers whom we had noticed in the Astoria Ballroom, accompanied by a somewhat scrofulous local-looking lad named Finbarr or similar, who turned out to be her husband.

Nevertheless, despite the presence of a wedding ring on her finger, we had zoned in and buzzed around her like fruit flies. Showing little or no regard for her husband's sensibilities, we'd tried to steer her gently down the path of infidelity. Worryingly, she was having none of it and treated our gauche advances not only with the contempt that they so richly deserved, but with a light laugh and a toss of her glorious blonde mane. Nor did her husband seem at all put out by our obvious lusting after and chatting-up of his lawfully bedded wife. He knew something that we didn't. He knew that she loved him and wasn't interested in anybody else. This was an alien concept to us, one that we had difficulty assimilating. After this shameful start we were forced to the conclusion that the couple were just nice people who were genuinely friendly and liked us. Once we had entered this cul-de-sac we relaxed and became accustomed to seeing them whenever we were in the area.

We became genuinely friendly too. A departure and an odd feeling.

When we got to know them a bit better we learnt that Helen's mother had recently bought, renovated and opened a hotel just outside of town and maybe we would like to stay in it sometime as her guests?

We accepted immediately.

On the appointed day, on the way through to a gig in the immediate vicinity, we checked in.

The hotel itself nestled on a small exposed rise, perfectly situated to catch the gentle breezes that whipped in mercilessly from the northern Atlantic Ocean, a body of water that seldom bothers to differentiate between winter and summer.

The Mabel Arms was more of a motel really, with spacious forecourt and redbrick walls; a single-storey edifice housing some twenty-odd almost-comfortable rooms. There were stables out back and scattered horses lolling about the adjoining greensward.

Guests seemed few, apart from the occasional travelling salesman scuttling down a corridor.

As we toted our meagre overnight belongings into the foyer, the proprietor skipped gaily down the stairs.

Mabel was in her early forties and looked not unlike a slimmed-down Hattie Jacques. She had a pleasant round face, sensuous eyes, stout though shapely legs, an ample bosom and a mischievous laugh that verged on the cackle. Her long blonde (dyed) hair brushed her shoulders in an attractive manner, accentuating her full lips from which protruded a black pungent cigarette; Sobranie, I believe. I had encountered these during my tenure on the docks in Derry during my Exotic Cigarettes Period, when I cut a swathe through the international world of pilfered fags, amazing my friends and often making them sick. The worst was a Russian brand of black tobacco that was smoked through an attached hollow piece of cardboard. This brand felled two people who should've known better.

But I digress.

Mabel was, of course, English. Her husband had conveniently expired without prior warning but not before prudently making financial arrangements that granted her enough money to escape the hurly-burly of Birmingham, enabling her to set herself up in these pleasant though barren, windswept surroundings.

I noticed that she eyed us up individually when we checked in, the way a dealer would check out yearlings at Goff's. Heads tend to notice these things.

'We won't be back here until late tonight,' one of us ventured, sometimes a problem in hotels run by those new to the business.

Mabel smiled, 'I expect you'll need a little nightcap, then?'

As the band's spokesman at the time, and in the interest of avoiding embarrassing misunderstandings, I pointed out that late meant three o'clock in the morning.

'That's fine,' she murmured, a little huskily.

We played the gig and found her waiting for us when we arrived back at the hotel, shortly after three a.m. She was wearing a form of kimono and high heeled shoes, an odd but encouraging combination in any man's culture.

She thoughtfully opened the bar and drinking commenced. We were pleasantly surprised to observe that no money was asked for and, crucially, no record kept of units of alcohol consumed. As night inevitably turned to day and some of us dropped out due to the heady mix of fatigue and whiskey, the more alert amongst us noted that, although Mabel was matching us drink for drink, she remained perfectly sober.

The rest is hazy. I went to bed about nine in the morning after tipping a plate of scrambled eggs onto my lap.

The last man standing at the bar was our saxophonist who was last heard mumbling shite about John Coltrane's reeds. I crawled upstairs and found my room.

Breakfast was served at two o'clock on the same day. Mabel was accommodating, brisk, business-like and friendly.

Only when she disappeared into the kitchen did shards of the truth emerge.

Apparently, after I had gone to bed, leaving our sax player to wind up proceedings, Mabel had closed up shop and carried his still-conscious form to her bedroom. Like some kind of trophy.

Now, in the harsher lunch-time light, he revealed fresh welts on his back and muttered ecstatically about bull-whips, manacles, leather dildos, arcane forbidden acts, foul couplings of the most heinous kind and declared that he had never heard of, never mind experienced, such depravity as was displayed to him in Mabel's inner sanctum.

We were thrilled.

It was, however, difficult to believe. She seemed so motherly today. But welts speak louder than words. We decided to believe his account and deduced that, because he was not particularly attractive to women, he must have been chosen because he was the last man standing at the bar. There could be no other explanation. Nothing else made sense. Next time we stayed there we formulated a set of rules. Each man must drink exactly the same amount as the next man. There was to be no sobriety, holding back, or pouring drink into convenient potted plants. Let the last man standing harvest the fruit of his labours.

Democracy at work.

One man, one bullwhip.

It became a sporting fixture.

——

'So what was she like?' asked Lashback, impatiently.

'What do you mean?' Eddie.

'What did she do to you when she got you upstairs. With the whips and stuff?'

'I don't know. I never made it.'

His gaunt eyes swung in my direction.

'What about you?'

'I never made it to the finish either. Always fell at Beechers.'

'Beechers?'

'Never mind.'

Lashback looked at us with barely disguised disgust.

'Pussies!'

And I suppose we were.

Whilst we'd been talking to Lashback, O'Brien had left the pub with his woman.

He never could wait.

It was eleven-thirty and the barman was trying to empty his pub. This was late for him if he didn't have the Garda Síochána greased.

It was time to gather up the minstrels and play the gig.

Like the Turtles. Happy together.

It was almost midnight when we arrived back at the hall. Billy and Ray would wait for O'Brien to return from his short shagging expedition. They would appear onstage on time. O'Brien was nothing if not professional. He'd make sure that his charges showed up. Just as well. If left alone, Ray and Billy were more than likely to say fuck the gig and tie one on, especially with a few charvers in tow. It was the Way of the Northerners. Especially if the gig didn't hold out much promise. But O'Brien knew this well and would act accordingly.

The absence of vehicles outside confirmed my earlier fears. The People Sitting Outside in Their Cars had gone elsewhere. A collective decision had been made and it was not in our favour.

As we entered the hall through the small side door leading to the backstage area, we could hear the enthusiastic pluckings and yelpings of the relief band. By the sound of their dismal efforts echoing emptily around the hall we could tell that we weren't going to have the pleasure of playing to a full house. 'If they're not in by midnight, forget it,' was the mantra of the ballroom owners.

Backstage, I sneaked a peek down the hall through a curtain that was partially pulled back.

There were no more than a hundred people in the hall, most of whom should by now have reached the point of realising that they had come to the wrong gig. However, traditional show-band punter behaviour dictated that once a person had paid at the door, that person would remain until the death. The die had been cast. Anyway, most of them had neither the transport nor funds to facilitate a change of scenery and venue before everything closed down at two a.m.

People who attended country dance halls in those days constituted a mixed bag. I could see the usual gaggle of girls, maybe forty strong, forming a semi-circle round the escape hatch that was the entrance to the womens' jacks. Only local girls partook in this ritual, requiring, as they did, a bolthole through which to, well, bolt when approached and hit on by an unsuitable male. And the local girls were very adept at isolating and getting away from these undesirable suitors, of which there were always several cruel waves.

Woe betide the rural pretty ones, I always thought. Especially the ones who hadn't the sense to fuck off to England or Dublin. This was a dangerous time of the night.

Local men entering the hall at this point in the evening, after having been thrown out of the local pub, would be cock-a-hoop with confidence by dint of a bloodstream pounding with copious amounts of stout and whiskey. At this stage of the proceedings, the rampant male would feel at the height of his powers. Having consumed all the alcohol that would be available to him this night, the average buck would lunge at women repeatedly until the initial rush of the drink died in him, which usually occurred about an hour-and-a-half later, rendering him more fatigued than inebriated. During the intervening period he would, if ugly, nasty, brutish or short, have been rejected by every halfway decent looking girl in the hall.

Remember, too, that girls exclusively occupied one side of the dance hall. The other side was the exclusive preserve of the male. A man who decided to ask a young lady to dance had to cross the no-man's land that was the dance-floor. Every brave step he took would be closely observed by his peers. He would, of course, have singled out his target or prey. The prey would know he was coming for her. If he was acceptable to the target, the target would look away but move closer to the rim of the pack so that he may access her all the easier. His offer of a twirl accepted, the two of them would swirl away to the admiring and often envious gaze of onlookers.

If however, as was more often the case, the man was badly dressed with piss-stains on his trousers, unattractive, drunk and glazed of eye, and had propelled himself by automatic pilot towards the prettiest girl in the hall, she would, of course, rapidly discern the oncoming cretin and swiftly disappear into the sanctity of the ladies' toilets. The oncoming man would not be deterred and, though the batch of women would recoil and shrink away, much as a shoal of fish will dissolve in all directions at the approach of a predatory seal, the less nimble would be grabbed and gruffly asked to dance, only to tear themselves away emitting small shrieks. The drunken would-be dancer would find himself marooned, aware only of the distant barracking of his mates. He would turn and take the long walk to the gentleman's crapper where he would regroup and re-emerge as if nothing had happened, ready again to do battle.

The drunken man who assailed the early pack of women who congregated in the vicinity of the women's loo was an extreme case, the kamikaze pilot of the ballroom world. Far more impressive indeed was the moment when most of the men in the hall decided that the time was right to charge the knot of women in a body.

Similar in nature to People Who Sit Outside In Their Cars, the Communal Lunge was triggered by a number of factors, one of which was the opportune Slow Dance.

The Slow Dance fulfilled the dual purpose of (a) giving the band a breather, and (b) allowing men immediately to jam their deprived crotches against those of women to whom they had not been introduced.

But not just any announcement of a slow dance from the stage would trigger the Communal Lunge. The timing had to be right. All being well, the first Lunge would come at about 12.30 a.m. (assuming always that the dance would end at 2 a.m.).

The battery of women surrounding the epicentral entrance to the ladies' toilets would be swollen by now, as would the ruck of males straining at the leash at the other side of the hall. The mens' eyes would feed hungrily on the womens' small areas of exposed flesh. The women would not dare look across the floor at the men but instead would chat nervously amongst themselves.

An oily showband head would announce a slow dance. Male ears would prick up, much as the ears of the lion on the hunt will stiffen at the faint whiff of zebra musk. The women would brace themselves.

A man with bad hair would warble the opening line of, say, 'I Left My Heart in San Francisco' and they were off!

Time was tight. Only a brief window of opportunity was available. The zebra were fording the river now, slow and vulnerable. Lions and men must move now or fail.

Each man now an island, he would move determinedly towards his selected mate.

'Where little cable cars climb halfway to the stars.'

Because so many men were approaching simultaneously, the batch of women felt besieged and began to undulate, like an amoeba disturbed.

Many of these women were trapped in the crush, unable to escape from those particular thrusting men whom they didn't want near them. Mustn't weaken, they thought. Men were coming at them in waves, the front runners having the best chance of success. It was the ones who came behind who were usually doomed, having given the women time to writhe away from their outstretched horny hands.

One side of the hall was now a thriving mass of squirming humanity, the only direct route to the ladies' toilets often cut off by the brisk traffic.

Then, suddenly, it was over. Rejected men scurried rapidly back to their own side of the hall. This was not the humiliating solitary trek of the lone operator. There was comfort to be had by retreating in numbers, no shame in mass withdrawal. Fags were lit and relaxing poses adopted whilst they convinced themselves that they were rejected only by the girl with whom they wanted to dance, whereas in their black hearts they knew that they were also rejected by the girl who stood beside the one they were after, and by the one beside her as well. Only then would the valiant male admit defeat and figuratively toss in the towel.

I always felt sorry for the small knot of dishevelled girls left behind after the Communal Lunge. During the skirmish, any half-way attractive girl would be asked onto the floor by at least one bloke who was not completely obnoxious. She would dance with him rather than be left behind. Because left behind were those whom nobody wanted. The uglies, the dogs and the wallflowers.

It's a ruthless world.

Around the floor would dance the triumphant men, each with their prize, reluctant partner though that prize might well be.

'The morning sun may chill the air... I don't care...'

———

But this would happen later here in St Brigid's Hall if a few more punters came through the turnstile. I threaded my way backstage to what passed for our dressing-room. Lashback had overturned the mutilated cigar-store Indian and was perched on what remained of the brave's chest cavity.

'This is some shit-hole, wha'?' he rasped

'Looks like a long night in front of us,' I agreed.

Harpo and Pat had installed themselves in a corner around a small table they had found somewhere. They were playing cards.

'Mightn't be too bad,' said Harpo, out of the side of his mouth. 'There's one or two real dogs sitting in front of the stage.'

'Really?' I replied, interested now. 'Hadn't seen those.'

'Check them out,' suggested Harpo, lighting an untipped Senior Service cigarette. They're pretty special.'

We were equal connoisseurs of both natural beauty and bone ugliness. Just two ends of the one spectrum. And who was to say which end was superior?

'These gigs aren't getting any better, are they?' Eddie muttered, wriggling out of his trousers.

19

The day it was decided we should resort to white suits was the day, in my opinion, that it was all over. When the band was first formed we had opted not to wear any kind of uniform. That was for the other cheesy fuckers.

Grass skirts, suits or anything in that line would smack of regimentation. Rebellious, you see. Fired by heady times. This was, after all, the seventies. We were all free now, weren't we? Had Janis Joplin died in vain? But even these times were changing. And even Dickie Rock, arguably the most avaricious of the major players, had adopted casual clothing on stage.

If Dickie did it, money couldn't be lost.

There was another school of thought, of course, maintaining that Dickie's decline from true icon status after the splintering (but prior to the mowing down) of the Miami Showband coincided with his abandonment of the suited-and-booted image that had elevated him to the pinnacle of whatever it was he was aiming for.

Dickie, for one, suited a suit, one made from that stretched sleek mohair material, so snugly tailored that it looked like it might restrict movement but didn't. With city-boy matchstick legs sternly encased in what resembled a shiny plaster cast and an upper torso reminiscent of that of the Tin Man from *The Wizard of Oz*, Dickie was quite the spivved-up gurrier as he strode menacingly about the stage, revealing a lop-sided snarl, strangely dead eyes and a faintly lobotomised aura about him that always made me feel uncomfortable. Dickie onstage always looked liked an alien being experimenting with the audience, a other-worldly visitor trying to divine what these malformed organisms below wanted from him.

As Dickie has grown older, his body has aged but his head hasn't. These days, when I hear him hold forth on television talk shows, I imagine I see a trace of barely concealed bewilderment on his face, perhaps the only outward sign of a sense of wonder that a man can maintain for so many years and still not be rumbled by the proletariat.

Spit on me Dickie, indeed.

Most Dublin bands suited wearing suits. Northern bands too. Not so sartorially elegant were those from smaller cities such as Cork, Limerick, Galway or the like. Bands from the real sticks clung to their suits as well but mostly looked like they were either coming from Mass or going to a wedding.

By the early seventies most bands wearing suits on stage were inclined towards the more sober cut. The zany days of the sixties when sartorial crimes were more numerous had long since passed. My brother Johnny once formed a band called The Emperors, whose band suits were made of a seemingly indestructible silver material, the likes of which I had never seen before, nor have I since (although I was reminded of their texture recently whilst researching a documentary about the materials found in the New Mexican desert outside Roswell in 1947). Like the Roswell shards of allegedly alien kit, these band suits didn't seem to crease or wrinkle either, and sprung back to their original shape if rolled into a ball. The Emperors also wore purple suede shoes which I greatly admired, and shirts of the crassest yellow.

I used to creep into Johnny's room when he was out, knowing that his silver suit was present, hanging nobly in the wardrobe. Like the space-suited Earthlings in the film *2001: A Space Odyssey* in the Moon crater housing the monolith, I would run my hands over the material and could only speculate as to the provenance of this wondrous fabric.

I even tried the jacket on once.

Now I knew how Elvis felt.

The collective Brown and O'Brien wore white suits with frilly shirts. We also wore fiddly little leather boots with high heels to make us look taller and therefore more desirable. We had once experimented with casual wear. Encouraged to buy whatever we thought was 'trendy,' a cash allowance was duly allocated for the purchase of the clobber.

All that was accomplished was the development of a general tendency not to shave before going onstage. We soon wore little else but our carefully selected 'casual' gear' onstage and off. Some of us slept in the clothes and we ended up looking more scruffy and dirtier than before.

So here we were, wiser counsel having prevailed, back in our white suits. It was for the best, it was claimed.

This was, after all, show business.

It was time to go on stage.

Billy, Mike and Ray showed up perilously late, the three engaged in a protracted discussion whilst they hurriedly pulled on the trousers of their white suits and struggled into their carefully ruffled shirts.

Problems with the women in the pub had arisen due to O'Brien's early exit with his charver.

'It's all the same to me,' said Billy, puffing on a cigarette as he buttoned up his shirt. 'I don't care one way or the other.'

'You couldn't wait could you?' said Ray caustically, giving O'Brien a cold hard look.

'Get it while you can, I say,' replied a cheery O'Brien.

'But that's going to mess me and Bill about,' retorted Ray. 'Can't you see that? The three of them will probably fuck off now that you've dabbled.'

'Bill doesn't care. So what?' replied O'Brien. 'Plenty more where they came from.'

'It's all right for you,' said Ray. 'You've already got your hole.'

'How sophisticated,' laughed O'Brien.

'You can see Ray's point,' laughed Billy, nonplussed. 'In all probability they will indeed probably fuck off now. Couldn't you have waited until after the gig. It would've been more mannerly, not to mention gentlemanly.'

'Mannerly!' chuckled O'Brien. 'It was eating the leg off her.'

Ray was getting more annoyed. It had been a while since he had himself dabbled, I guessed.

'The other two will know that you've fucked her. And they'll know that you're telling us about it now. Mine's and Billy's will feel under pressure. They'll probably fuck off because of it. You know that.'

'Maybe mine won't tell the other two,' ventured O'Brien.

'Little chance of that. And if she doesn't, do you think they won't figure it out?' said Ray.

'He's right,' said Billy to O'Brien. 'You've messed it up. The one that you fucked mightn't tell the others straight out but they'll know for sure when she suggests going elsewhere. Then they'll know and that you'll have told us. As Ray rightly surmises, our two will feel under pressure and the three of them may well disappear. You should have waited until after the dance.'

He was right. Given any group of three women lined up for the use of members of the band, one found that they preferred to be fucked simultaneously in order that the guilt may be distributed evenly. If one was fucked prematurely it may ruin the night for others who must labour in the same vineyard.

Ray would be upset if his woman absconded. He had bought her a total of four brandies. From his point of view, this constituted a substantial investment.

A stentorian voice was heard from the corner.

'I'll go down and ride the three of them if it'll make you guys feel any better.'

It was Lashback, of course

And he would've had a stab at it too, had he received the slightest encouragement.

Harpo had packed up his cards and was fussing about like an old woman.

'On after this, lads,' he said, referring to the last batch of three numbers being played by the relief group. 'Get yourselves organised!'

He was, of course, completely ignored.

I lifted my bass guitar from its case, slung the ragged leather strap over my shoulder and caressed the maple neck fondly with the palm of my left hand. The smoothness of the neck and thick strings soothed me. This guitar was my most treasured possession, and not solely because I owned little else of value. I was emotionally attached to it. Musicians should feel that way about their instruments, I thought. I had a pretty expensive Marshall stack too but didn't give a fuck about that. As far as I was concerned, it was just a bunch of wires, speakers and wood. This Fender Precision bass guitar was special to me—a work of art. I bought it when it was one year old and still have it today. It stands in a corner of this room as I write. Despite decades of rough handling and regrettable neglect, its naked wood shows no mark or blemish, itself a minor miracle when we consider that this instrument has defied bombs (from both sides), been rough-housed by the Army, fallen out of vans, been left behind at airports, used as a weapon to repel angry punters storming a stage, and often lost but always found.

Nothing feels like a Fender Precision bass guitar. This one was made in 1964. 1964 was a good year to be a Fender guitar. A product of the vintage years from 1950 to 1965, each guitar lovingly examined and supervised by the legendary Leo Fender (the Stanley Kubrick of guitar design) himself until he relinquished control to corporate Japan in 1965.

There is no sound like that of a Fender bass guitar. With the right amp and a favourable prevailing wind one can hear and feel the deep, pure, forceful wave of sound wafting from behind one onstage, a wave that often sets the trouser legs flapping in an agreeable manner.

Lashback, though marginally insane, was a good drummer. This is important not only to a bass player, but in the overall scheme of things. The drums and bass are the spine of any band. The wonderful thing about a bass player and drummer who can really synchronise their playing is that when the two gel well, the efficacy of the pairing is not stand-out noticeable. It feels right when it feels right and is missed only when unaccountably, and as is usually the case, it doesn't feel right. When it doesn't feel right, it can't be fixed. That's why most showbands clanked and sounded amateurish.

But let us not travel any further down that particular anorak road.

I always enjoyed the first twenty minutes or so of any gig, chiefly because we were a good band. We worked well together. Somehow, the disparate personalities within the band amounted to an acceptable whole. No matter how many 'fucks' Ray spat through the bell of his saxophone, the real notes were true enough. Pat was reliable on trombone, Eddie exceptionally talented on lead guitar, me happy on bass, O'Brien warbling nasally though in tune (when he eventually bounced onto the stage), and Billy, on keyboards and elastic-band-bound tenor saxophone, holding the thing together by his musical instinct during rehearsals, and by his quiet authority during the gigs.

Our vocal harmonies were quite good too, though nothing approaching the standard set by Billy's previous band, The Freshmen. We could never hope to equal that, a fate that Billy was resigned to but which didn't seem to bother him much any more. I suppose he had more or less given up.

We were good but nothing special. The first twenty minutes of most gigs were enjoyable because of the natural but temporary energy of the band, coupled with the fleeting curiosity of the dancers, who would often linger in front of the stage listening to the first few numbers.

After a while they'd get fed up and drift off in search of someone with whom to breed.

And so it was to be tonight.

We tripped onstage as the relief group smirked and strode off. We had become sloppy and no longer bothered to tune our instruments prior to going on stage. There was a time when we regarded this as important. Prior preparation of this nature meant that we could immediately launch into our first number without the messing about involved in tuning up onstage, the tootling saxophones, tinkling guitars, the rapping snare drums, and the general hubbub of a band that doesn't care about wasting as much time as they could get away with.

The punters were normally patient though and, who knows, maybe some of them regarded our slapdash attitude and offhand manner as evidence that we were, er, cool. But, hardly, not in Saint Bridget's Hall, with its surprising murals, mutant tea-lady and corrugated iron superstructure.

When we were ready, Billy hunched over the electric piano and sang the opening bars of Elton John's 'Rocket Man.' He sang the idiot words of the song beautifully.

I plonked the first note of the night and we were off.

Ray's back was hunched too, but his hunch was natural, the laboured stoop of a man who was stranger to any form of exercise or healthy living. He stood stiffly, one leg seemingly shorter that the other, holding his flute. Lifting the instrument to his mouth, one shoulder higher than the other, he looked hideously deformed but played sweetly, not that any of the punters cared one way or the other.

They were already drifting away, Elton John's 'Rocket Man' not, I thought, an inspired choice as a means of holding their attention. This crowd would have required something earthy to grip them, something more visceral. Perhaps something related to hurling or tractor-care.

All had melted away except for a small knot of men who had assembled below the left side of the stage, where I traditionally and presently stood. They gave me their undivided attention.

I knew why they were there.

This scenario used to bother me greatly in the past but I had become accustomed to it by now. It had been ever thus. In the beginning, the phenomenon had caused me a great deal of soul-searching but I had been forced to come to terms with the fact that it was real and, though decidedly unwelcome on my part, something that I had to deal and live with. And anyway, if handled sensibly and diplomatically, it was easily coped with. The confusion lay within.

The small knot of men were members of the local gay community. 'Gay', of course, was not a word in use in 1972. Other less complimentary terms were certainly in vogue, terms more colourful but, alas, no longer acceptable in this modern day world, so 'gay' these men shall remain.

Depending on the size of town, village or townland serviced by any particular ballroom, a varying number of gay men would show up at any given dance. If you like, the only gays in the village. They obviously knew each other so, presumably, there would be no surprises there. They came principally to check out the city slickers in the band and there was nothing wrong with that. They would, naturally, keep a sharp weather eye out for any members of the band whose gaiety could be rumbled by their collective antennae.

Alas, this is where I came in.

I am not gay. Never have been. I rush to add that I am neither glad nor displeased to be ungay. I would doubtless have handled the gay card had it come my way. Nor do I disparage those who have been dealt it.

God, however, in His wisdom, has decided that whatever signals I transmit are picked up loud and clear as evidence that I am one of the favoured ten per cent. I have long since ceased to figure out why this should be so but have decided that this should remain a road less travelled.

Is it a look, something with the hands, facial expression, the way I stand, how I move when I plonk the bass (perhaps lack of said movement?), a certain aura?

All I know is that it started early. Initially I dealt with by this by ignoring their attention and avoiding them when they approached me after dances. I was further aggravated by the fact that they scared women away.

I learned to deal with these men in the way I would deal with them today. I would not avoid their eyes. Nor would I stare at them more than was strictly necessary. I would meet their gaze when required until I had identified, excuse the expression, the ring leader.

After a few numbers, usually at the end of the second set of three songs when we had warmed up, I would approach the front of the stage and beckon the leader.

'You're barking up the wrong tree, kid,' I would inform him. 'I'm straight. Y'understand? You're wasting your time.'

I would then point towards Lashback. 'That's your man,' I would suggest.

The news would be relayed back and attention focussed temporarily on the formidable Lashback.

Lashback wasn't gay either but his wild eyes and hungry look usually scared them away.

Billy would light his first cigarette on stage when he lost interest. None of us followed suit. It was something we felt he had licence to do. It was unprofessional, of course, but Bill had been through all that shite and had come out the other end a legend. Let him do what he wanted. He was going to move on to something else soon anyway. Something that wouldn't involve any of us. He couldn't tolerate this forever.

His electric piano was a mass of little black burn marks, the legacy of former fags.

O'Brien and Pat were the only two who maintained a show of interest throughout the night; O'Brien because he probably felt that looking keen was the only thing he had left, and Pat because he was afraid somebody might notice him slacking and somehow engineer his demise. Not that there was much chance of that. Even our manager didn't come with us any more, sitting on his fat arse in Dublin on the look-out for the next big thing, which certainly wasn't us.

The gig proceeded and those of us who cared little lapsed into the usual torpor.

Two hours can be a long time when one would rather be somewhere else.

There were about two hundred people in the hall by now, most sitting listlessly about on chairs pushed together the entire length of each side of the hall. The only way of passing the time was to observe. I had developed the eye of a social anthropologist.

These punters formed the usual cross-section of humanity.

Most visible were, of course, the drunks. They usually stood, smiled and swayed, fearful of sitting down lest they might have difficulty getting up again or, worst of all ignominy, falling asleep with lolling head.

Most of the local boys, as we have discovered, hunted in strung-out packs and were easily identified by their purposeful, long strides, ruddy faces, not-quite-plastered-down hair and large knobbly hands.

And there before me was the usual elderly, probably smelly bachelor, who even now was systematically making his way down the serried ranks of seated girls asking each one in turn to dance, only to be spurned by a thoughtless giggle, turned away-head or a firm 'feck off' from the rougher colleens.

Then there was the Good Jiver. There was usually at least one of those, especially in the summer. The Good Jiver rarely remained at home whilst there was an England across the sea, or, at a push, a Scotland. He could be seen back home in the summer months, wearing Beatle boots, bell-bottom trousers and an ill-fitting high-collared jacket in a primary colour. His shirt may well have been purple. His hair, however, was sometimes problematical due to the prevalence in Donegal of naturally clenched hair. Many men in Donegal are blessed with small, tight, wiry, black curls, the type of hair that whitens prematurely.

Why this hair pigmentation should be so, I am not qualified to say, but I imagine a drop or two of Spanish/Moorish blood may have entered the picture somewhere along the way. Links between Spain and Donegal were strong in the past. And people do speak of the Donegal Dubhs as a thriving but scattered sub-section of the county 's ethnic mix.

Thus is it inadvisable for such a man to grow his hair long. He may find himself with an inexplicable Afro. Which may look great on Phil Lynott but weird on the wrong white man. One need only cite Luke Kelly in his pomp.

It's the women who make life in Donegal worth living. Many of them have dark hair too, frequently worn long and straight, silky alabaster skin, delicate features, long legs made for the dancing and the kind of soft voice that would melt a heart of stone.

Tonight, though, these women were extremely thin on the ground. Female talent seemed scarce in Saint Bridget's.

The ugliest ones perched, as usual, in front of the stage with their backs to the band. I've always thought of this positioning as defensive. Only the pluckiest of men would stride across an empty dance floor into the very teeth of a blaring band to risk being publicly rejected by a girl who was no great shakes in the first place. The ugly ones felt safe there. No-man's land in front and their rears covered to their satisfaction.

The three women snared in the hotel by Billy, Ray and Mike were seated halfway down the hall, away from the other clientèle but close to two men who didn't look like the rest.

They weren't locals. This was self-evident due their smooth tans and the fact that they were wearing clothes that fitted them.

Quite a few French, German, Spanish and sometimes, Italian tourists were to be found wandering about Donegal at this time of year.

The tourists were talking to the three women. I saw that Ray had noticed this too. He seemed uneasy. His prophesy seemed on the verge of coming true. If these women were indeed of a mind to fuck off because O'Brien had jumped the gun, who better to fuck off with than men whose armpits didn't hum.

I hoped he wouldn't be called upon to play a saxophone solo anytime soon.

O'Brien was otherwise occupied Winking at the Wall. This was something he did during the first ten or fifteen minutes of each performance.

I always made a point of studying him Winking at the Wall. There was something artfully thespian about it. Let me explain. Although Billy was the main attraction, he didn't cause any fuss, nor did he receive any special treatment or big introduction when we took to the stage. He just shuffled over, sat down on his piano stool and looked for somewhere to park his fags and matches.

When we were ready, Bill would warble the first ditty, in this case, as we may recall, 'Rocket Man.'

Billy would then half-heartedly introduce O'Brien, who would then bound enthusiastically onto the stage as we stumbled into the intro of, say, James Taylor's 'You've Got A Friend'. Songs recorded by those with nasal voices seemed to suit O'Brien best (his voice did have a disconcerting Donald Duck element to it that was difficult to ignore) whereas Billy was more comfortable with the more ethereal material.

In mid-stride, O'Brien would snatch the microphone from the stand in one practised movement and perform his little goat-dance, part of the repertoire of tested and proven 'shapes' that he had developed and polished over the years. He would then lift his eyes, look to the left hand side of the hall, smile broadly and wink heartily at the blank wall. He would sometimes point at it too, often mouthing a fulsome greeting to the masonry, wallpaper or wood panelling, as if spotting an old friend or admiring fan of long-standing lurking in the audience.

He would, of course, have spotted nothing.

He did this because he did not regard it prudent to leap onto a stage in a country dance hall and smile, wink and gesticulate at people whom he didn't know and, crucially and especially, at people who may not like him very much.

Those who saw this instant but risk-free bonhomie may conceivably have taken to him. This is why he did it. Only after ten or fifteen minutes when he had time to scan the punters' faces and separate the friendly from the openly hostile did he deign to address his smiles, winks, and insincerely pointed index finger at functioning human beings.

There are a number of reasons why singers have to be careful. Especially randy ones.

I have mentioned earlier the potential risks involved when O'Brien did his gay schtick in country halls. When he risked this, he might attract the unwelcome attention of unimpressed macho heterosexuals who might conceivably choose to take a pop at him later.

His shapes would, of course, fail to register with the bunch who were keeping a pink eye on me at the side of the stage. O'Brien didn't fool them for an instant.

Which hardly made me feel any better.

Here was a good-looking man mincing and pouting for all he was worth but the boys didn't buy it. They instinctively knew his shapes were empty. They only had eyes for me.

This was upsetting on every conceivable level.

Also, O'Brien had to be wary of the girl who was with her boyfriend but who wanted to fuck O'Brien. This was a double-edged sword. Men, rural or city-dwelling, have a sixth sense when it comes to suspecting that their girlfriends are of a mind to stray with the main man in the band.

One had to be particularly alert during 'slow' dances. Girls who were dancing with boyfriends but who fancied one of the guys in the band would position their partner in such a way that they (the soon to-be-cuckolded partners) had their backs to the stage as they approached the bandstand, allowing the female to gaze lingeringly at the object of her desire. The recipient onstage would use this window of opportunity wisely by deploying an arsenal of winks, louche smiles, mouthing of compliments and, more crucially, pointing at his wristwatch, accompanied by the raising of a quizzical eyebrow (translation—can you get rid of that sodbuster by the end of the dance?).

But the person on stage must exercise caution. A man dancing with his girlfriend with his back to the action should sense that he is vulnerable. One side of his blind head may detect a smile tightening his girlfriend's facial muscles, the faint raising of a female hand in a small involuntary wave, the movement of jawbones as the owner forms silent words or, worst of all, the sudden involuntary pressure of his girlfriend's groin grinding against his. This is a sexual reflexive action common among primates who see someone they wish to fuck whilst in the humdrum embrace of someone whom they have tired of fucking.

If the boyfriend was astute and succeeded in detecting one or more of these signs he would, at an appropriate moment, suddenly swing his girlfriend the full 180 degrees so that he could catch red-handed the man onstage. This was where certain thespian skills came into play. The man onstage had to betray no hint of guilt, surprise or embarrassment. He would instead continue to leer, smile, mouth and point at the couple directly behind the dancer who suspected him. The male partner would thus concede that he was mistaken. He would welcome the relief.

He wanted to be wrong.

There was a point midway between our usual two hours on stage when showbands of our ilk were expected to do something special that might entertain the crowd. After all, that's why the word 'show' preceded 'band.' I blame The Clipper Carlton for this.

The Clipper Carlton were just another band operating out of the small Tyrone border town of Strabane in the early fifties. One of the band members had a relative in America who had access to musical arrangements for groups with brass sections. These high-level arrangements would be used in night-clubs and concerts by people like Danny Kay, Johnny Ray, Frankie Laine and other big recording and cabaret stars of the day.

The Clipper Carlton were basically a Dixieland jazz band. It was hard work blowing four and five hours a night for the little money that was in it at the time and nobody seemed to give much of a fuck about Dixieland music which traditionally was always more fun to play than to listen to.

The band member whose relative had access to these rare arrangements decided that, if the Clipper Carlton could conjure up something similar to a cabaret act that wasn't too taxing or strenuous, it would be (a) something different, but more importantly (b) would give some of the guys in the band a respite from playing relentless and exhausting jazz—a breather. No more importance was attached to it than that.

So this is what they did, spicing up the musical cabaret with a little comedy (the band fortunately had two members who together constituted an acceptable Laurel and Hardy). The arrangements were employed and the band prospered to such an extent that the 'showband' as we know it in Ireland, was born. The prototype was there for all to study. Money flowed into the coffers of these unassuming men from Strabane. They had created a monster.

And, as already mentioned, the standard line-up of the Dixieland jazz band lent itself admirably to the reproduction of almost any pop song that would appear in the charts during the next twenty years.

So, the showband was invented by a guy who knew somebody in America who imported the idea of doing cabaret in order to give musicians from Strabane a rest.

Upon such noble foundations dost the Irish showband industry proudly stand.

These early abominations left a lingering historical expectation amongst punters that showbands should do something special halfway through their nightly stints.

Our answer was the drum solo.

Only drummers and psychopaths enjoy drum solos. But these blatter-fests have long been regarded as acceptable fare to place before the punters as 'speciality entertainment'.

Amongst the ranks of the more intelligent heads, drummers are often regarded as sub-human. Most musicians secretly believe that drummers are psychotics who are attracted to drums as an acceptable means of channelling an innate violence that would normally be expended in a manner more dangerous to the rest of us. I personally think this view harsh but not entirely without merit.

Lead singers, too, are regarded as different in that they harbour an unnatural longing for the attention and approval of the general public. It's surprising how often lead singers reveal unhappiness as a child or some marring incident in the past that preys upon their minds. So maybe it is true that the wounded need an audience.

It is no coincidence that many bands during this period, when asked at Army check-points how many musicians were in their number, often replied, 'Six, and a drummer.' This was generally followed by raucous laughter from all but, yes, the drummer. The singer wasn't even included in the joke. Singers ranked below drummers. It's a needlessly cruel world.

I have never understood the popularity of drum solos. I can appreciate a show of artistry from early greats like Gene Krupa up through Joe Morelli, Philly Joe Jones and even Ginger Baker but why anybody would want to stand and watch, never mind listen to, Lashback pound his drums with an artless venom for ten minutes was beyond me.

He, of course, thrived on the attention.

We regarded drum solos as merely an opportunity to smoke whilst the punters seemed to display a dull interest in them if only to appreciate the brute strength required to hammer those skins for the prolonged period of time required to smoke two cigarettes and have a piss.

'Land of a Thousand Dances' by Wilson Pickett was a good song from which to veer into a drumfest. The hysterical nature of the song, plus the nursery-rhyme singalong lyrics (na, na, na, na, na, na etc.), plus the frequent mention of crippling dance-steps favoured by our black brothers i.e. Watusi, Mash Potato, Pony, Jerk, and, of course, the Alligator, none of which were in the average Donegal dancer's repertoire, helped set the mood for the solo thrash of drumsticks.

After the drum solo had exhausted itself we were usually galloping down the home straight. The last hour was the period during which my mind tended to wander. By that time I had, as per my nightly regime, already decided who amongst the dancers had the distinction of owning the reddest face, biggest nose, stickiest-out ears, most debilitating limp, most repulsive manner, biggest tits, and the droppedest arse—the shortest man and woman in the hall having already duly been located, selected, noted and catalogued.

With thirty minutes to go, I usually reached the terminal stage where I began to ponder the motives of whatever God is up there and turn to a review of the Saviour's alleged active role in arranging and supervising everything we do. Standing on a stage for hours staring dully at masses of shifting, revolving and revolting people will do that to a man.

It usually started when my eyes swept the floor in search of the Most Horrible Person in the Hall. To be chosen as such was quite an honour as competition was usually stiff.

Now, to be fair, the person might have been male or female, but I have to admit that this noble sobriquet rarely went to a woman unless she had something spectacularly obnoxious going for her.

It is difficult to give an example of what this special quality might be, except to say that one recognised it immediately when it appeared. Men usually came tops in this category due to the fact that whatever redeeming qualities a potential candidate might have harboured had usually been cancelled out by a surfeit of drink.

Nor did looks play a major part. In the past, my choice of Most Horrible Person in the Hall often came down to a couple of drunken men, one of whom might conceivably have been conventionally handsome.

It was about demeanour, natural hatefulness and general behaviour. A certain amount of boorishness, coupled with a brash self-confidence and a bad suit was a good start. Being a show-off dancer usually garnered high points and a hint of open contempt for the band would often favourably tip the scales.

Once the chosen one was selected, I tended to study the winner at length. Whilst I looked at him carefully, I found myself contemplating something along the lines of… of all the millions of sperm released by this man's father and the terrible journey they had to embark to lay siege on his mother's egg, he was the only one who made it.

Imagine what the others were like.

These were the kind of dark, anti-social thoughts that worried me more and more and led me to the inescapable conclusion that I had to quit this business.

The dance was nearly over. I could tell this by the fact that Billy had smoked all his cigarettes and thrown the empty packet on to the floor. We had already played Lindisfarne's 'Meet Me on the Corner' twice, 'Help Me Rhondda' three times and, always a sign that we had thrown in the towel, Chuck Berry's 'My Ding-a-Ling'.

Our work was almost done here.

We finished off with a couple more Chuck Berry numbers to finish off the jivers, after which O'Brien subsequently bade the punters a cheesy goodnight, urging upon them the usual God-assisted safe passage home.

Ray was anxiously scanning the hall in search of the three women. They were nowhere to be seen. He fixed a gimlet eye on the door of the ladies' toilets.

'They've fucked off,' I said, leaning my bass guitar up against my amplifier.

'I knew they would,' he spat. 'Fuckin' O'Brien…'

'Looks like they linked up with those foreign-looking guys,' I added. 'Did you see that happening?'

'Fuckin' O'Brien. He couldn't wait. They were in the bag. Weren't they?'

A hint of self-doubt.

Unusual for Ray.

He was taking this multiple defection badly.

Fuckin' O'Brien was standing in front of the stage handing out photographs of himself to a couple of girls who, judging by their similar sets of prominent teeth, may well have been related.

I was quite tempted to walk over and say, 'Mike, Ray's really pissed off because that charver you shagged in the car before the dance seems to have talked her mates into going off to be fucked by dusky foreigners.'

I fought the impulse. The girls with the teeth might not have understood.

Pat was handing out photographs too and being friendly and self-effacing. I was never any good at that and usually desisted.

Eddie and Lashback had already gone backstage, uninterested in any form of post-gig public relations exercises.

Billy was trapped on his piano stool by a man in his forties wearing a jumper who had produced a handful of photographs from the small ersatz leather bag he was toting. I could see the man was a professional bore by the way that he had artfully cut Billy off from any avenue of escape from his piano stool. By the desperate look on Billy's face, I could tell that little about the snaps held his attention.

I could've gone over and rescued him but I didn't bother.

Let him suffer.

I grabbed a bottle of lemonade from a crate behind the drums, jumped off the stage and sat on one of the chairs lined up on the right hand side of the hall.

I stared for a while at eight or nine young bucks competing for the pleasure of kicking an empty cigarette packet across the floor.

There was much violence in their horseplay.

Fuck this. I had to get out of this business.

I was then aware of two girls standing beside me.

They were young, about nineteen years old. Not bad looking. Dressed like tarts, terminally mascara'ed but acceptably blonde. I hadn't seen them at the dance. They must have entered the hall as the gig ended.

Always a good sign.

They looked like poachers, sweepers-up. In at the heels of the hunt to bag the band. Always to be welcomed.

'Hello,' said one.

'Howerya!' I replied.

'Givvus a swig of your mineral.'

I handed over the bottle of orange.

'There you go,' I said.

'Have you got another bottle?' said the other one.

'I might have. Why?'

'If you givvus a bottle you can ride us.'

'Hold on,' I said. 'I'll get a crateful!'

Life is short and few of us are sure if there's anything afterwards.

Things didn't improve much as time passed. I sensed that this was going to be our last year. It was clear that as a band we were almost finished. Whatever credit that remained from the past successes Billy Brown and Mike O'Brien had enjoyed in other bands had now been squandered by this current unenthusiastic line-up.

A spent force somehow depleted to begin with, all that was left for us now was to do the rounds until the gigs dried up.

I was quite happy to go along with this, of course, having no perception of the concept of tomorrow. It never occurred to me that I might have to take a job in the real world if the band folded and no other gig turned up. It never occurred to me that I might starve, protected as I was by lack of knowledge of, or interest in, the real world.

I found youthful ignorance such as this a wonderful thing. Total irresponsibility is a gift from God that should be encouraged, nurtured and cherished.

Being totally irresponsible provides one with a cloak of invulnerability. Only those who fear the worst are condemned to experience it. The others normally escape.

As a band, we were pretty much at our lowest ebb. Talk began of a new start elsewhere. It's this fucking country, was our mantra. It's dragging us down to the level of the others.

Problem was that we didn't see ourselves as entertainers. With the exception of O'Brien and possibly Pat, none of us were interested in show business. We were marooned in the wrong racket.

It sometimes happens that people become interested in music without first considering the thought that by taking up an instrument, they will someday have to stand up in front of people and play what those people want to hear. Not all of us want to do that when we start out.

When it reaches the point of how bad that can be, every musician has his Room 101.

My rat scratching at the wire mesh in a cage in front of my face was …weddings. I made an unbreakable, solemn promise to myself that, as long as I drew breath, I would never play at a wedding.

Why weddings should be such anathema to the likes of me chiefly boiled down to the fact that the father of the bride (as used to be the case. I don't know about now), for probably the first time in his life, hired a band for which, tradition dictates, he was duty-bound to pay. Because he felt that he had 'bought' this band, he would regard it as his personal plaything for the day and, drunk with power, demand that the poor bastards play all his favourite tunes. The father of the bride would not understand that the band may not be familiar with, and usually indeed loathe, some of the songs he was determined to hear but this was but a minor consideration when he felt the need to point out that it was he who would pay the piper, if he chose so to do.

I have heard poor bastards in wedding bands attempt Viennese waltzes, obscure Bulgarian polkas, songs recorded by Gracie Fields and Donald Peers, The Dave Clark Five's 'Glad All Over', Dave Dee, Dozy, Beaky, Mick and Tich's 'Zabadak', right down to, and I do not exaggerate, Arthur Askey's 'The Bee Song'.

And sometimes nappy-wrapped children belonging to the wedding guests would wander onto the stage and interfere with proceedings. The parents let them roam at will. Woe betide the musician who deemed one of brats worthy of a clip about the ear.

Weddings make an honest musician feel less than worthless as a man.

During such gigs are alcoholics formed.

And it's not just me. I have spoken to others who have their own Room 101s, recurring nightmares about being dressed as Hawaiians playing on the back of a moving lorry doubling as a float taking part in some local carnival or other whilst all the people they have ever known line the streets to point and jeer—Dante's Carnival….

And others hallucinate about having to take a gig in a circus band. This is a particular horror for trombone players who know that they may some day be forced down this road of despair by economic considerations. There was a time when the trombone was especially valued in circus bands, the loud *glissando* a reliable indication that a clown's trousers had dropped to the ground, or that the arrival of a herd of beach-ball-balancing elephants was imminent.

Alas, this trombonist's nightmare no longer holds any currency. Circuses have dispensed with all human music-making. The seven-piece circus band is no more. Consigned to history in the company of the high-buttoned boot.

Of course, the ultimate horror lurks in every sensitive musician's Room 101. The beast beats on the door intent on slouching towards Bethlehem.

Because one may yet, if one has expired internally, eke out a living as a session musician…

But again, I digress.

Talk began to be heard more frequently that we might do well in Canada. The initial idea, that we could conceivably undertake a short standard tour, lacked merit. We didn't want that, knowing as we did that a tour of Canada would involve six weeks playing in an Irish club in Toronto called the Maple Leaf, a gig that usually ended in fistfights or a general sapping of the will to live.

I had been down that road before and had enthusiastically taken part in the gradual trashing of a house that had been kindly granted to a bunch of us for the duration of our stay. The end result was not pretty. But we'll get to that dirty business soon.

Gradually it was mooted that perhaps our talents, if we took the trouble to hone them, might be appreciated in regular so-called cabaret clubs in Canada, not your bog-standard Irish clubs at all. We were grasping at straws and we knew it. Canadian punters no more wanted an Irish band refusing to play 'Seven Drunken Nights' than they wanted a Romany gypsy band playing Beatle covers. They wanted Irish bands because they were Irish bands.

There was management balls talked that a tour such as this could be easily set up. Our manager was keen to encourage this for reasons of which I was immediately suspicious. He was not the most cultured, having learnt his trade in the snooker rooms of North Dublin, where I'm sure he bloodied a nose or two during the course of his formative years.

Not for him an appreciation of the four- and five-part harmonies we enjoyed working on, certainly not for him the doomed jazz-based material that we were most comfortable with, or the tinkering about with obscure efforts of barely known American songwriters with attitude.

His reasoning was clear: band attract crowd = good band = money in the till. Band not attract crowd = bad band = less loot to go round.

Nor could I find fault with this fiscal logic. The problem was that he never talked to us in those terms. It was as if he assumed that we wouldn't understand practical matters. Instead, he chose to lie to us, telling us only what he thought we wanted to hear even though we were well aware that we were being lied to. And he, well aware that we hated his guts, responded by treating us like children, which was exactly the right thing to do.

We wanted to change things but we couldn't be bothered putting in the work necessary to make these changes occur. We had seen too much.

He was content now merely to humour us.

Anyway, all Canada talk had petered out by the end of August 1972 and, because we had a whole week off (another ominous sign) I took off for Ibiza where the craic was reported to be good.

This indeed proved to be the case and after a week of blissful though blistering sun, little sleep and vaguely illegal behaviour I boarded a plane back to Dublin.

Things had moved on apace since I'd gone. On my return I found that we were scheduled to leave for Canada in two days' time in order to fulfil a number of gigs at Canadian nightclubs.

I was suspicious but had too many things to occupy me these remaining few hours. I was told that in order to be eligible for a Canadian Musician's Union card, we had to apply for the status of 'Landed Immigrant', in other words, to emigrate. This smacked a little of Black '47 to me until it was explained that we would not be allowed to enter the country to play gigs if we said we were musicians (a shade ironic), but we could gain entry if we pretended we didn't know each other and were emigrating separately to Canada in order to practise various bogus trades allocated to us by our manager. Then, once we got there, we would see about getting our hands on musician's union cards.

I was an electrician, as I recall. I think Ray was declared a joiner. I remember thinking that the emigration guy at the other end didn't have to be Sherlock Holmes to smell a rat when Ray the Joiner shuffled up to the desk. Equally unlikely was Billy Brown, the Plasterer, or the House Painter, Mike O'Brien.

Eddie had decided not to come with us. He'd had enough. I was sad to see him go. We had been to hell and back. I was going to miss him.

So, we went without a guitarist. But, what the hell, we were going to do cabaret. I don't suppose we really knew what the word meant. In our ignorance we believed that people in other countries would be more civilised than what we'd been used to and would appreciate good music played well. This new world didn't have a name so we called it Cabaret. What we really expected was to play somewhere where a man and a woman might sit, have a real drink, and listen knowledgeably to the band, rather that break a leg trying to dry-hump his partner whilst trailing her across a puke-spattered floor. In the fantasy world of Cabaret everything was flexible. And, anyway, what was there to fear when we had men who could plaster, join and elect? Nothing could touch us.

Yes, we were incurable dreamers.

I naively thought that all this procuring of documents and union-card trickery and lies might be difficult to accomplish in two days but I was wrong. Our paths seemed conveniently smoothed. I couldn't believe how easy it was to go to various government buildings and tell lies to officials who seemed to have no brains. They seemed to believe everything we said. Documents were stamped and shuffled. We didn't realise that we treading a well-worn and faintly criminal path.

I remember saying to Ray, 'Fuck this, let's not go to Canada at all. We can get a job on a building site here. Seems a shame to deprive this country of our skills. Let's practise our trades and make a fortune. We've the papers to prove it.'

He grunted.

We flew out via Shannon. In separate seats on the plane. We were told to dress down and look like working men. I don't think we were entirely successful.

As soon as we arrived in Canada and lied our way through Emigration, we were whisked into a van and driven to an Ontarian town called Chatham, wherein lived a man of Irish extraction who was president of Chatham Musician's Union. It was within his remit to issue musician's union cards to us all. I didn't see money change hands, which doesn't mean that it didn't, but a number of valuable pieces of Waterford Crystal did. There seemed a demand there for the distinctive glassware.

Oh, the machinations and deceits of us Irish abroad.

Our first gig was in two days' time in Kingston, Ontario, and having been assured it wasn't a regular Irish club, we were more than a little excited. In the meantime we holed up in Toronto, at the time a dour city much loved by Nordies.

We didn't have much time to look around the country before we had to play. I didn't mind. I'd been here before. It was no accident that Toronto was known as West Belfast. Many who fled the Troubles in horror ended up there. It was America with a heart.

During the seventies, many people from Northern Ireland felt a little uncomfortable in the United States. Maybe there was something frightening about being treated the same as everyone else, something frightening about knowing that a man could get a job at any time. Too much choice and little to complain about can be unsettling for people accustomed to living on the edge and being fucked about for sport.

Reared on a diet of state benefits and no responsibility tended to render one unsuitable for the cut and thrust of America, where there is only the quick and the dead. Canada was a tad more understanding, more laidback, and full of what a later President of the United States liked to refer to as 'Northern Irelanders'. That was just enough to make it preferable to the States.

It reminded Northern Irelanders of home. Everything shut down on a Sunday. If they'd put locks on the children's swings in the playground on the Sabbath, half of the Northern Irelanders still at home would've been across the Atlantic in a flash.

The ubiquity of our warring tribes was emphasised when we pulled up outside our hotel.

A nondescript man happened to be walking past operating a small improbable dog on a lead. The man looked vaguely familiar. So did the dog. Both turned out to be from Derry. He, a guitar player who'd fled the coop a year before and, it, the dog he had brought with him.

It wasn't easy getting rid of either of them. If his dog hadn't been with him he might never have left.

People who have been away from Home for a while want to talk about Home to people who have just arrived from Home and don't want to be reminded of it.

———

I shared a room with Ray.

Because Ray had spent quality time in America, he seemed to revert to a past life and mode of behaviour that I hadn't seen before.

His accent changed overnight. He began to drawl and mumble incoherently. Worryingly, the only word I could make out when he spoke was 'nigger.' Each time he enunciated this none-too-pleasant word he would cackle loudly.

Turned out he'd spent much time in the past with some hard-drinking rednecks in Texas who drawled in a similar mumble. The only word Ray claimed he could ever make out was, well, 'nigger'. It was obviously a word used often.

I asked if his old redneck friends happened to be in the habit of wearing white robes and erecting burning crosses in people's lawns but there was no getting through to him now that he had become an American. And every once in a while, for no particular reason, he would mutter the words 'women should be obscene and not heard.' He would then laugh heartily and briefly.

Matters were not helped by his starting to drink constantly as soon as he got off the plane. On the pretext that no beer could be bought in Ireland that didn't bubble fizz back down his nostrils, he drank Labatt's and Budweiser, as we are now encouraged to say, 24/7.

He then contrived to eat no solid food but pizza, demanding the most foul melange of toppings—ill-suited ingredients mixed with salami, olives and anchovies.

Our room eventually became a loathsome pit of offensive odours, compounded by his habit of using his discarded pizzas as accidental slippers.

You may not be familiar with the concept of accidental slippers. Here's how it works.

After an evening and half a night spent in bed drinking countless bottles of beer, screaming at a malfunctioning television set that was wisely chained to the wall and seemed to show only episodes of *The Time Tunnel*, and drunkenly ordering three pizzas at a time, Ray would eventually pass out at three or four o'clock in the morning.

An hour later his abused bladder would demand a trip to the bathroom. Ray's spindly legs would swing lithely over the side of the bed and, unerringly, plant a foot each in two of the unfinished, discarded pizzas that were littered about the moth-eaten carpet. He would then rise like Lazarus and stumble towards the bathroom, fumbling at his underpants. Because of the gooey and, therefore, highly adhesive nature of the toppings that remained on the surface of each pizza, these Italian specialities clung to Ray's feet and accompanied him to the bathroom. He looked like a man wearing snowshoes.

Having relieved himself, Ray would return to his scratcher still wearing the pizzas on his feet.

Back into the bed he would drunkenly sink. Sometimes the pizzas disengaged from his feet, but not always.

The presence of pizzas clinging to the soles of his feet did not faze Ray in the least until he woke up in the morning and realised, with a scream, that large clumps of dough were still clinging doggedly to his extremities. Nor did he ever learn not to put pizzas down where he might step on them en route to a piss.

He reminded me of our budgie in Derry when I was little. The budgie had unprecedented freedom for the era and was allowed to fly around our kitchen at will. It always settled on our mechanised clothes line, which stretched across the kitchen roof at an elevation and position directly over the open fire in order to take advantage of the rising warm air. The budgie appreciated both the altitude and the heat but unfortunately always chose to sit beside the pulley mechanism that was used to lower and raise the clothes line. This proximity to the pulley meant that, whenever the mechanism was operated, the swift movement of the cogs would remove a few feathers from the budgie's arse. The budgie would then shriek wildly and take off in a panic, usually crashing into our kitchen window. Losing tail-feathers in such a violent manner was obviously a painful business but in due time the bird recovered and remained in its cage for a while. However, when new feathers grew, the bird was back beside the pulley.

In the fullness of time the bird found itself with yet another denuded arse.

Some budgies don't seem capable of learning from experience.

Ray and the budgie were as one.

We all went a little crazy during those two days.

We passed the time by hitting the local bars where Mike and Billy discovered that they were irresistible to Canadian women who had never seen or heard the likes of them before.

Perhaps a harbinger of good times to come, this was a confidence-booster for them but a downer for us, we who were free of natural charisma and needed to be identified as heads to be in with a shout at all.

I found that my accent was a liability. Not having anything of any consequence going for me, I was further disturbed to discover that Canadian women thought I sounded like a person from Newfoundland.

For Newfoundlander read Culchie.

So, in a way, it didn't matter if I roomed with Ray or not, as I usually arrived back alone anyway.

I didn't mind sharing a room with Ray because, although eccentric, he was the least trouble and didn't need to be humoured or talked to. His own private world was quite enough for him. At least he didn't insist that others live in his world too. That was a plus as far as I was concerned.

Billy and Mike had rooms of their own, due to the anticipated heavy throughgoing traffic.

Lashback lodged alone too, as a precaution, and Pat and Harpo roomed together, oddly suited.

Ray and I were odd bedfellows but it seemed to work.

Ray was alone no matter who was in the room with him.

————

Our first gig was a nightmare. We had, of course, insisted that we not be specifically advertised as an Irish showband. It was therefore somewhat of a shock to see, outside the featureless motel that we were appearing at in a town called Kingston, Ontario, a shamrock-encircled poster announcing us as the greatest showband in Ireland, just off the plane.

We were undeterred. We would soon surmount that, we reasoned. We were also intrigued to hear that we were booked for two weeks, playing Monday to Saturday. The nightly gig was scheduled from eight p.m. to one a.m. and we were expected to play four half-hour sets on the hour and one final hour-long set from midnight until closing time. The rest of the time we were expected to 'work the room.'

Those hours seemed a tad long but, happily, were mercifully spread out, a total of three hours' playing time—an hour more than we were used to. We would survive.

This was when we began to see more of our manager, who had hitherto been rarely spotted. He now did all the talking to the guy who ran the club, a rather unpleasant-looking perspiring gentleman who constantly chomped on a small cigar. We were mildly excited. We had never 'worked a room' before and, in our innocence, enquired as to what this might possibly entail. We were told that, rather than race to the bar when we had a break, we were expected to be friendly to the customers, doing the rounds of the tables, being charismatic and out-going, encouraging them to buy more drink. We should have known that this wasn't for us. This was Butlin's Redcoat territory.

We did not pick up the warning signs. I talked to some of the bar staff on the first Monday afternoon and asked about Kingston itself. Turned out there was a large maximum-security penitentiary just outside of town.

Apparently it was habitually referred to as 'Alcatraz North,' which in itself should have sounded alarm bells. The inmates had practically destroyed the prison in a four-day riot a year before during the course of which two inmates were killed.

'Quite a joint,' said the flaxen-haired and almost-attractive, short, corpulent girl behind the bar. I pondered whether or not to stake an early claim on her. Best to have something lined up. After all, two weeks is a long time and who knows what's ahead.

'Doesn't affect this gig, of course, does it?' I asked.

'Does what?' she replied, absentmindedly.

'The, ah, prison thing, the penitentiary. Does it affect the gig?'

'Not really, except that a lot of the prison visitors tend to stay in this motel overnight.'

'And what are they like?'

'What do you figure they're like?'

'Dunno.'

'What kind of people do you think make up the nearest and dearest of the most violent criminals in the country?'

'I would hesitate to guess. Don't like to judge.'

'Fair enough.'

She turned to wash some glasses. I noticed she had a dropped arse. A fine example. At least nine points from a possible ten. First trans-Atlantic one I'd seen.

However, in our innocence, we rather looked forward to the gig. This was going to be different.

No more mud-spattered marquees, no more freezing fingers reluctantly dragged over icy, lacerating steel guitar strings, no more mercenary priests, crones in kitchens, knuckle-trailing promoters, wooden-topped nymphomaniacs, village idiots, long-nosed crotch-twisters, broken-down heaters on wintry nights, cloudy bottles of orange crush, bare arses poking from speeding coaches, no more Big Tom, Wee Mick, Spit on me Dickie, Bullfrog Larry, no more uniformed assholes, idiot comedy drummers, sly sentimental country singers with an eye on a quick buck, no more 'Jerusalem', 'Simon Says' and no more houses with white-washed fucking gables.

There were eighty to ninety punters scattered about the bar when we went on stage to play our first set.

We kicked off gently—a song by the Beach Boys ('California Girls', as I recall), a jazzy instrumental, a Mose Allison blues followed by an acappella version of 'Smoke Gets in Your Eyes', then a Swingle Singers track followed by an instrumental blues. So far, so good. Audience seemed a little quiet. Nobody danced despite a small, square, hoofing area. But that wasn't unusual. The drink hadn't taken hold yet. It takes time to be somebody. Punters didn't applaud much. Just a smattering here and there that quickly died out. We thought that strange. But, oh, well, maybe that's the way it is out here. Alternative cultural mores. It was early.

But we did think it odd that we didn't receive more of an appreciative round of applause than the one hand clapping we heard at the conclusion of our first set.

We stepped from the stage and, unsure of precisely how to 'work a room', headed in the direction of the bar. Before we reached it our manager ran over and quietly escorted us to a smaller, more private room backstage.

He was about to open his mouth when the cigar-chomping guy who ran the place stepped in. 'What's that shit you cocksuckers are playing?' he roared.

'It's what we do,' whispered O'Brien, clearly taken aback.

'Not here you don't. You're an Irish band, right?'

Billy opened his mouth to stutter.

Our manager answered for him.

'We are, yes.'

'So, play some Irish shit or get the fuck out of here!'

The message was clear.

'Certainly, sir,' replied our manager, smiling grimly. 'Just a misunderstanding. Leave it to me.'

So this was cabaret.

We somehow managed to struggle through the night interspersing our, as we thought, interesting set with just about every Irish song, melody, air or riff that we could bring to mind. The crowd turned out to be a little gamey, especially as the night wore on. A bunch of Irishmen working on a construction project not too far away mingled with the relatives of innocent murderers and rapists who were, of course, wrongfully imprisoned in Kingston penitentiary.

We spent the next day rehearsing 'The Bold O'Donahue', 'Danny Boy', 'Boolavogue', 'The March Hare', 'The Siege of Ennis', 'Does Your Mother Come From Ireland', 'Galway Bay', and, uniquely, 'The Hokey-Cokey'.

We did this because we knew that we wouldn't be paid if we didn't. We quickly realised that not being paid three-and-a half thousand miles from home was more fraught with difficulty than not being paid in the Crystal Ballroom in Dublin.

Holy fuck, I mused. This is worse than the Galtymore in Cricklewood.

It was all over from then on. All that followed was but the reflex kick of a dying band.

We soldiered along, increasingly worried that our money supply seemed extremely limited. This was explained away by our manager who cited a precedent seemingly unique to Canada whereby bands weren't paid right away but were called upon to be patient for a number of weeks whilst various financial procedures were adhered to.

This was bollocks, of course. I sensed there was a game plan at the conclusion of which we would find ourselves, as it were, sucking the hind teat.

In the meantime we were magnanimously granted ten dollars a day to live on. Our next port of call was a town called Sudbury in Northern

Ontario. Sudbury was peculiar in that it wasn't safe to walk the streets due to the ever-present whiff of something akin to sulphur emanating from the surrounding nickel and copper strip mines. We could feel the fumes of Hell (sorry, Sudbury) erode our gums as strolled and breathed. We only strolled once and learned to breathe outdoors only when necessary.

The area had been so denuded by this form of mining that, it was rumoured, astronauts from the NASA Space Programme used the terrain to practise negotiating the pock-marked, crater-strewn and slightly less arid surface of the Moon.

And so it was here that we came upon the door to our manager's door swinging open one fume-blest early morning. He had fled the scene. Maybe the sulphur had done its work.

Alas, no. Our money must've come through. And the middle-men had been cut out.

Us.

All we had left was the return half of our air tickets.

Billy and Pat decided to use them. They had wives and girlfriends and lives at home.

We had little or nothing to go back to that couldn't wait.

And now there were four.

We had the nucleus of a band and union cards.

I had one dollar in my pocket and faced with the choice of buying a double cheeseburger and French fries or a packet of cigarettes – the latter prevailed.

A cheeseburger was merely a cheeseburger, but a cigarette was a smoke.

After much discussion it was decided that we would throw ourselves at the mercy of the man who ran the only serviceable Irish club in Toronto, the Maple Leaf Ballroom.

The owner, John Gilligan, was a man with whom one didn't mess. A wealthy man with fingers in many pies, he was from Mayo and went to considerable lengths to entertain the Irish community in Toronto by bringing over showbands and imprisoning them in his ballroom for up to six weeks at a time. He was a benevolent but strict man who demanded high standards of conduct and personal behaviour.

A lengthy stint like this at Gilligan's ballroom meant that the bands could chill out for a while and then return home free to lie that they had been on a six-week tour of Canada and had been greeted everywhere by rapturous hordes.

The main attraction of going to Gilligan was that he had a house which he allowed visiting bands to use as a temporary base. O'Brien seemed to have an 'in' with Gilligan.

'Let's stay here for a while,' Mike enthused. 'We'll pick up a guitar player, get our hands on an agent and see what happens. Gilligan will see us right. If we offer to play for him for free for a few weeks when we get organised, he'll bankroll us and let us stay in Pinewood.' (35 Pinewood Avenue off St Claire in Toronto, also known as Gilligan's Folly.)

I was uneasy, for very good reasons. I had once spent six weeks at Gilligan's Folly two years before with, I'm afraid, The Chessmen. For reasons not unconnected to the spirit of voyeurism, we had decided to remove all the doors. This decision was occasioned by members of the band bringing women back to the house and keeping them to themselves. It was decided that there was to be no more privacy for anyone. It was all for one and one for all.

This was but the start. Much drink was consumed during the weeks ahead. A kind of madness descended. Orgies were encouraged and boxing matches between members of the band were staged and bet upon. Blood was spilt. Parties lasted for days, furniture was splintered, windows shattered and the house deteriorated at an alarming rate over the period of six weeks. In fact, at the conclusion of our stay, we realised we had to get out before any of Gilligan's people realised the extent of the damage inflicted upon his generously granted accommodation.

This we did. I hadn't seen him since.

He had another good reason to remember me. Down the street from 35 Pinewood Avenue lived a black family who spent much of their time sitting on the front porch. We would have sat on our porch, too, if we hadn't partially dismantled it. Amongst them was one of the prettiest girls I had ever seen. She was about nineteen years old and my heart melted. After a few days sparring, I asked her if she'd like to come to the Maple Leaf Ballroom with me.

She said yes.

I picked her up at the appointed time and walked proudly down the street.

She looked wonderful.

We were stopped at the door of the ballroom by a bouncer.

'Where are you going?' he rasped.

'Inside,' I laughed.

'Not with her, you're not.'

For a moment I didn't understand.

'Why not?'

'You're not going in with her.'

The girl spoke softly, 'Never mind,' she said. 'I'll go home. You go ahead.'

'We're going inside,' I said.

'You are,' he said. 'But she isn't. House rules.'

'What house rules?'

'You know as well as I do.'

I didn't. But I could guess.

'If she doesn't get in, I'm not playing tonight.'

'Whatever you like,' said the gorilla. 'It's up to you.'

I lost of course.

Gilligan was called and was appalled at this open challenge to something that he thought best not aired in public.

I had to give in when it was explained that if I didn't play that night the band was in breach of contract.

I left the girl back home.

Her family were not best pleased.

It was my fault. I should've known.

No blacks allowed. Turned out they didn't let Polish people in either. The Famine Diaspora had taught us much.

———

We arranged to see Gilligan in Toronto.

As we piled into his office, I kept as low a profile as possible. O'Brien did all the talking and all seemed well. Everything worked out as O'Brien had hoped and we now had a place to live and regroup. All we had to do was find a guitarist.

Gilligan looked at me for a long time. He had blunt features but a sharp eye.

'Do I know you?' he said.

Fuck.

'May do,' I replied.

He looked at me coolly.

'I remember you. You're the little bollocks with the nigger. You fuckers wrecked my house.'

This occasioned a little tension in the room.

'I apologise,' I said. 'It seemed a good idea at the time. Won't happen again.'

He smiled and threw O'Brien the keys to the house.

Fair play to the old bastard, I thought. He understood

We eventually found a guitarist and went back on the road. It was a dull, pointless existence. We were living and travelling just to keep body and soul together. I remember thinking that I didn't have to do this. I could go home and sign on the dole in Derry and sleep in my own bed until noon when my mother would creep in to the bedroom, tap me gently on the shoulder and ask if I'd rather arise and go downstairs for my dinner or have it brought up to me on a tray. This was a dangerous train of thought. At least there was nobody being blown up in Canada, unless they happened to work in the sulphur mines of Sudbury.

Everything changed in a place called Peterborough.

We'd been on the road for a while and I must've sang 'I Can See Clearly Now' a thousand times. All I knew was that I never wanted to hear 'Proud Mary' again.

Peterborough was a largish town seventy-five miles north-east of Toronto. We were playing for a week in a bar frequented by the usual white trash: check-shirted rednecks, line-dancing showboaters, short-skirted honeys and drink-addled regulars.

On one or two nights during the week I noticed a man who didn't look as if he belonged. He was tall, had long fair hair, aquiline features and was clad in a long expensive leather coat which he never removed. He didn't drink much and, unusually, seemed to be listening to the band.

We didn't go near the bar, of course, having long rejected any pretext of 'working the room.' Never work a room if the punters don't like the band. Things can happen.

Anyway, it was never a good idea to sidle up to lumberjacks whilst wearing a white suit and frilly shirt. It tended to bring out the worst in them.

So, although curious, I didn't speak to this man.

I was therefore surprised to observe him approach towards the end of the gig on Saturday night, our last night. We were due to take off next day for our next gig in London, Ontario.

He proffered a hand.

'Howdy.'

Howdy? The last person I heard saying howdy was Hopalong Cassidy.

'Hello,' I said.

'The name's Dwayne English. Been checkin' out yo' band.'

He spoke with a Texas drawl. I hoped he wasn't going to start talking about niggers. I might have to call Ray over.

'Wanna do an audition?'

'Pardon?'

'I play drums with a band called 'Ronnie Hawkins and the Hawks.' We're rehearsing at Ronnie's ranch outside of town. We're down a bass player. Domestic problems. Interested?'

I hadn't heard of the outfit.

'What kind of band?'

'Rock 'n' roll. Gotta go. If you're interested in auditioning, somebody will pick you up outside at eleven o'clock tomorrow morning. If not, no sweat. But if I were you, I'd be there. Bye.'

And he was gone.

At eleven o'clock in the morning I was standing outside the front door of the bar. I hadn't seen a morning for years. I didn't like the look of it. It was bitterly cold and an icy gust raised fine dust that swirled down the deserted main drag. After all, it was winter and a Sunday to boot. My guitar case lay propped against the wall, the bass within more comfortable and warmer than I, swathed and protected as it was by the red velvet lining of the interior of the wooden rectangular box.

There was little risk of being rumbled. Of course, I hadn't told any of our lads that I was auditioning for another band. Just lied lightly and told them I was going to hook up with an old girlfriend and would meet them at our next gig the following night. This was standard procedure. By now we had learned to latch on to anyone who would fuck us and feed us on a Sunday, release us on a Monday morning and point us at the next gig. Thus did we avoid an unwanted Sunday-night hotel bill. And, anyway, none of the band would be up and about until well after lunchtime.

My feet were numb. There was a sizeable hole in the sole of my left shoe.

A very large shiny car rounded a corner nearby and fleetingly lost control of its back end on the frosty road as it turned in my direction. It was a very nice car indeed. I was no petrol-head but even I could ascertain that it was a Rolls-Royce. I remember idly wondering who the fuck would be driving a Roller in a kip like this. There was some kind of coat of arms etched on the front passenger door.

I prepared to watch it go by.

The car lurched to a halt beside me and down whined a darkened window. I could see the driver looking at me, squinting. He had long fair hair and was wearing a denim jacket and jeans. He looked like a thief, certainly not like a man who would own or even be hired to drive a car like this. Maybe he'd stolen it. I stepped back nervously.

He leaned over towards the window. He was smoking a joint. A little early in the day for that, I mused.

'You the Irish kid?'

I was looking at the motif on the car door. It was a depiction of hawk in flight. Very dramatic. Predatory. Ronnie Hawkins? Ah, I see...

Fuck, I thought. This is my lift.

'You Dwayne's guy?'

'Yes,' I stuttered.

He swung open the door.

'Jump in. Throw your axe in the back.'

Axe? Of course. Jazz/rock 'n' roll term for musical instrument.

I'd never been in a Rolls Royce before. It felt good.

He extended a hand.

'I'm Gary Lucas...'

'I'm the Irish kid.' I was getting the hang of this. 'Nice car,' I whistled. 'What is it?'

'Rolls Royce Silver Shadow. The Hawkmobile.'

'The what?'

'Hawkmobile. Belongs to the Hawk. Ronnie Hawkins.'

'I don't know much about Ronnie Hawkins.'

'You'll find out soon enough. Let's go.'

I remembered.

'To some kind of ranch?'

'No,' said Gary. 'Dwayne thought we were hanging at the place today. Nobody told him different. Ronnie went to his house in Toronto last night. That's where we're goin'.'

He pulled the black beauty away from the kerb and launched it down the road. He drove the car in a rough and careless manner. It didn't seem right. A fine machine like this horsed about by a man smoking dope.

'How far to Toronto?' I enquired.

'Hundred and fifty miles.'

He stared straight ahead. Silent. Still puffing on the joint. Didn't offer me any.

'Who's going to be there?' I asked.

'Dunno, it's a party. Regular thing. People in the business. Should be well alight by the time we get there.'

'Won't we get there a little early?'

'Two o'clock will be fine. The guests will have had lunch. After that it's time to boogie.'

'Will Dwayne be there? He's the only one I've met.'

'Sure.'

'Nice guy,' I said. 'Drummer, apparently?'

Gary beamed. Wildly. The dope was doing its work.

'One of the best there is. From Tulsa. Was with Leon Russell for a while. D'ya see that movie with Joe Cocker, Mad Dogs and Englishmen? That was Dwayne on drums.'

I was silent for a moment. *Mad Dogs and Englishmen* was one of the best rock 'n' roll movies ever made. And the shit-hot outfit featuring Cocker and led by pianist Russell was one of the best rock 'n' roll bands I'd ever heard.

What had I got myself into here? These were big-time players.

'What about rest of the band? Will they be there?'

'You're doing an audition aren't you?'

'So I believe.'

'Then they'll be there.'

It was time I asked.

'Who the fuck's Ronnie Hawkins?'

Gary hooted loudly.

'You're the only guy I've ever met needed to ask that.'

'I'm a slow starter.'

'Are you familiar with The Band?'

'I told you. Dwayne's the only one I've met.'

'No. I mean "The Band".'

I hesitated.

'You mean "Music From Big Pink", "The Weight", "The Night They Drove Old Dixie Down"? Bob Dylan's old band?'

'Right.'

'Yes, so?'

'They used to be the Hawks. Ronnie's Hawks.'

I stopped breathing.

'There's been a few Hawks since. This batch is shaping up to be the best one yet, since The Band.'

Gulp.

'If you make this audition work you're going to university, boy.'

'University?'

He was high now. The Rolls-Royce Silver Cloud shot down the highway at a great rate of knots.

Gary slapped his thigh and from the back of his throat rushed a rebel yell.

'*Yyyyyyyyyyiiiiihhehheeeee!* The University of Rock 'n' Roll!'

I gripped an armrest...just in case...

———

I must've fallen asleep. I wasn't accustomed to these early mornings. By the time I'd pulled myself together Gary had already taken my guitar case from the back seat. He opened the front passenger door.

'Rise 'n' shine!'

We were parked in a driveway of what looked like a large white colonial mansion with complementary Doric pillars.

I followed Gary up the rounded steps, entered an opulent hallway and turned left into a room from which I could already hear a loud buzz of conversation. It was a large reception chamber with elaborate wallpaper and ceiling frescos featuring naked cherubs. In the centre of the room was a raised platform draped in expensive-looking rugs upon which stood a grand piano, it, too, covered with painted naked cherubs.

I could sense a theme here. Sistine Chapel with gusto.

There were about forty people in various stages of disintegration, some standing about in small groups, others sprawled over randomly scattered sofas and armchairs.

This was an odd mix of humanity—standard hippies, men who looked like accountants, tarts, hard-faced women dressed in power trouser-suits, serious-looking long-haired young men who could only be musicians, a number of smallish children and a brace of dogs. They were all drinking and some of the women, in particular, appeared a little worse for wear. In my eyes, never a bad thing.

I had somehow lost Gary but spotted the lean figure of Dwayne English striding across the room.

He extended a bony hand and beamed.

'Made it, boy. Sorry about the confusion.'

I was glad to see even a slightly familiar face.

'Come meet the Hawk.'

He guided me across the room towards a small knot of people gathered around a large, avuncular, lightly-bearded figure, wearing black dinner suit, cowboy boots and a white Stetson hat.

He was smoking a very large cigar, which he removed when Dwayne leaned across and whispered in his ear.

His eyes lit up and he addressed his audience. 'We got one of them long-peckered English cats with us today. Watcha got to say for yourself, son?' The Hawk looked at me mischievously though twinkling eyes.

I'll rise to this, I thought. 'I'll accept the long pecker description. One out of two isn't bad. I'm not English. I'm Irish,' I said.

He laughed loudly and held out a horny hand.

'Well, that's what I'll call you, son. Welcome aboard, Irish. Go get yourself a drink and be somebody. Relax. Enjoy. We'll talk later.'

He turned back to his friends.

Dwayne brought me over to the bar.

I felt out of place.

'Where's this Hawk guy from? He's not Canadian, is he?' I asked Dwayne.

'From Turkey Scratch, Arkansas. Been up here ten years. The last of the good ol' boys. Started out in Memphis with Elvis. Took a wrong turn to rockabilly 'cause he thought rock 'n' roll was black music sung badly by white people—convinced himself that rock 'n' roll weren't nothin' but the sound of honkies getting it wrong. Toured the South with a black band in the late sixties. Only man ever to do that and come back alive. Got shot at a time or two, though. People down South called the band "The Redneck and the Four Fuckin' Niggers".'

There was that word again. If only Ray were here.

Dwayne continued. 'Hawk never figured that that Elvis white-trash rock 'n' roll would catch on. The Hawk's a legend. The rock 'n' roller's rock 'n' roller. Dylan's a fan. Zimmerman took to tailing the Hawk, writing down Hawkisms ever since the Hawk forgave him for stealing his band. John Lennon and Yoko lived in this house for three months. You just missed 'em—a crazy pair of motherfuckers.'

He handed me a large Jack Daniels. I needed a drink.

I was just a hair away from the big time. This truly was the Land of Opportunity.

There was a God after all.

The Jack Daniels went down remarkably well.

After one or two I started to mingle and relax.

A mistake.

Bad turned to worse.

I woke up next morning beside a shapely female form. I found out later that she was the ex-wife of Fred Foster, a record producer with Monument Records in Nashville, the man who co-wrote 'Me and Bobby McGee' with Kris Kristofferson, the man who discovered Roy Orbison. The Hawk was also on the Monument label.

I heard a knock on the door.

A cheery female voice.

'Come down to breakfast whenever you're ready.'

I looked at my watch. It was almost noon.

I had very little recollection of what had happened the night before. And could recall only vaguely how I'd ended up with the person asleep beside me.

I crept out of bed, dressed and felt my way downstairs.

The Hawk sat at a large kitchen table, still Stetson-clad and chomping on a cigar.

What appeared to be a maid fluttered about. There were children too and a lady whom I believe was Mrs Hawk.

'Morning,' I said, timidly.

The Hawk was reading the *Toronto Star*. He didn't look up.

'You drank all ma whiskey,' he drawled. He still didn't look up.

'Did I? I'm terribly sorry.'

It was as I'd suspected and feared. I'd blown it.

'Have some coffee.'

The maid fluttered again.

The Hawk stared at the newspaper.

I decide to take the initiative.

'Somebody mentioned an audition?' I ventured.

'No need to worry about that, son. You did that last night.'

A cold fist gripped my heart and twisted it cruelly within my concave chest.

I must've been drunker than I thought. Gods knows what I'd done.

'I-I-I-I don't seem to recall playing anything.'

'No, no,' said the Hawk. He put down the paper and looked me in the eye.

'No, I'm not talking about that. Shit, I already know you can play. Dwayne told me so. I trust his judgment. Your audition was about what kind of guy you are. Quickest way I know how to find out what a guy's like is to get him drunk and watch what happens. Saves time. Why wait for three weeks to find out whether you're an asshole or not? Get a man drunk and you see the real guy right away. You're no saint but, then again, I'm not looking for saints. You'll do.'

I sat silently, sipping coffee. I was having difficulty taking this in. It was the drink.

The Hawk winked. 'You've got my record producer's ex-wife in bed upstairs.'

'I'm sorry about that.'

'Don't be. She's over twenty-one years old. Way over, as a matter of fact.'

Thank you.

'So waddya say? Gary tells me you're playing in London tonight.'

'Yes…'

'Do you want to join the band?'

I was still hung over. Things were happening too fast.

'Come with me,' said the Hawk.

He led me outside the front door. The cold air hit me like a mallet.

'I need you in two weeks. Honour what commitments you have with your own band. Ring me when you're ready. Gary'll give you the numbers.'

I could see the Roller crunching down the drive.

It had been decided that it was time for me to leave.

The Hawk sucked once more on his cigar and exhaled with great pleasure into the frosty air. The Turkey Scratch Epicurean.

'You're gonna have to work hard, though. It's gonna be tough. This ain't no easy ride. You gotta want to be the best. I'll give you three hundred dollars a week to start with. We'll see what happens after that.'

I was living on a hundred.

He draped a brawny arm around my shoulder and looked left and right. He lowered his voice to a conspiratorial level. I could feel his beard rasp against my right cheek.

'That may not sound like much money to you,' he whispered. 'But if you join my band, you'll get more pussy than Frank Sinatra.'

University, here I come.

Hello, rock 'n' roll…

ACKNOWLEDGMENTS

- 'That's Amore' (page 151)
  Written by Harry Warren and Jack Brooks
  © 1952 Four Jays Music
  Peermusic (UK) Ltd, London

  Lyrics by Jack Brooks
  Famous Music LLC
  Administered by Sony/ATV Music Publishing
  All rights reserved. Used by permission

- 'I Left My Heart in San Francisco' (page 202)
  Words by Douglas Cross
  Music by George Cory
  © Copyright 1954 General Music Publishing Company
    Incorporated, USA
  Dash Music Company Limited
  Used by permission of Music Sales Limited
  All Rights Reserved. International Copyright Secured